information theory

mathematical
foundations
of information
theory

A. I. Khinchin

translated by
R. A. Silverman
  institute of mathematical sciences
new york university
  and
M. D. Friedman
  lincoln laboratory
massachusetts institute of technology

dover publications, inc. , new york

CONTENTS

The Entropy Concept in Probability Theory

On the Fundamental Theorems of Information Theory

The Entropy Concept in Probability Theory

The Entropy Concept in Probability Theory

(Uspekhi Matematicheskikh Nauk, vol. VIII, no. 3, 1953, pp. 3–20)

. In his article "On the Drawing of Maps" P. L. Chebyshev beautifully expresses the nature of the relation between scientific theory and practice (discussing the case of mathematics): "The bringing together of theory and practice leads to the most favorable results; not only does practice benefit, but the sciences themselves develop under the influence of practice, which reveals new subjects for investigation and new aspects of familiar subjects." A striking example of the phenomenon described by Chebyshev is afforded by the concept of entropy in probability theory, a concept which has evolved in recent years from the needs of practice. This concept first arose in attempting to create a theoretical model for the transmission of information of various kinds. In the beginning the concept was introduced in intimate association with transmission apparatus of one kind or another; its general theoretical significance and properties, and the general nature of its application to practice were only gradually realized. As of the present, a unified exposition of the theory of entropy can be found only in specialized articles and monographs dealing with the transmission of information. Although the study of entropy has actually evolved into an important and interesting chapter of the general theory of probability, a presentation of it in this general theoretical setting has so far been lacking.

This article represents a first attempt at such a presentation. In writing it, I relied mainly on Shannon's paper "The Mathematical Theory of Communication".* However, Shannon's treatment is not always sufficiently complete and mathematically correct, so that besides having to free the theory from practical details, in many instances I have amplified and changed both the statement of definitions and the statement and proofs of theorems. There is no doubt that in the years to come the study of entropy will become a permanent part of probability theory; the work I have done seems to me to be a necessary stage in the development of this study.

♯1. Entropy of Finite Schemes

In probability theory a *complete system of events* A_1, A_2, $\cdots$, A_n means a set of events such that one and only one of them must occur at each trial (e.g., the appearance of 1, 2, 3, 4, 5, or 6 points in throwing a die). In the case $n=2$ we have a simple alternative or pair of *mutually exclusive* events (e.g., the appearance of heads or tails in tossing a coin). If we are given the events A_1, A_2, $\cdots$, A_n of a complete system, together with their probabilities p_1, p_2, $\cdots$, p_n ($p_i \geqq 0$, $\sum_{i=1}^{n} p_i = 1$), then we say that we have a *finite scheme*

$$A = \begin{pmatrix} A_1 \; A_2 \cdots A_n \\ p_1 \; p_2 \cdots p_n \end{pmatrix}. \qquad (1)$$

In the case of a "true" die, designating the appearance of i points by A_i ($1 \leqq i \leqq 6$), we have the finite scheme

$$\begin{pmatrix} A_1 & A_2 & A_3 & A_4 & A_5 & A_6 \\ 1/6 & 1/6 & 1/6 & 1/6 & 1/6 & 1/6 \end{pmatrix}.$$

---

* C. E. Shannon, Bell System Technical Journal, 27, 379-423; 623-656 (1948).

Every finite scheme describes a state of *uncertainty*. We have an experiment, the outcome of which must be one of the events $A_1, A_2, \cdots, A_n$, and we know only the probabilities of these possible outcomes. It seems obvious that the amount of uncertainty is different in different schemes. Thus, in the two simple alternatives

$$\begin{pmatrix} A_1 & A_2 \\ 0.5 & 0.5 \end{pmatrix}, \quad \begin{pmatrix} A_1 & A_2 \\ 0.99 & 0.01 \end{pmatrix},$$

the first obviously represents much more uncertainty than the second; in the second case, the result of the experiment is "almost surely" A_1, while in the first case we naturally refrain from making any predictions. The scheme

$$\begin{pmatrix} A_1 & A_2 \\ 0.3 & 0.7 \end{pmatrix}$$

represents an amount of uncertainty intermediate between the preceding two, etc.

For many applications it seems desirable to introduce a quantity which in a reasonable way measures the amount of uncertainty associated with a given finite scheme. We shall see that the quantity

$$H(p_1, p_2, \cdots, p_n) = -\sum_{k=1}^{n} p_k \lg p_k,$$

can serve as a very suitable measure of the uncertainty of the finite scheme (1); the logarithms are taken to an arbitrary but fixed base, and we always take $p_k \lg p_k = 0$ if $p_k = 0$. We shall call the quantity $H(p_1, p_2, \cdots, p_n)$ the *entropy* of the finite scheme (1), pursuing a physical analogy which there is no need to go into here. We now convince ourselves that this function actually has a number of properties which we might expect of a reasonable measure of uncertainty of a finite scheme.

First of all, we see immediately that $H(p_1, p_2, \cdots, p_n)=0$, if and only if one of the numbers $p_1, p_2, \cdots, p_n$ is one and all the others are zero. But this is just the case where the result of the experiment can be predicted beforehand with complete certainty, so that there is no uncertainty as to its outcome. In all other cases the entropy is positive.

Furthermore, for fixed n it is obvious that the scheme with the most uncertainty is the one with equally likely outcomes, i.e., $p_k=1/n$ $(k=1, 2, \cdots, n)$, and in fact the entropy assumes its largest value for just these values of the variables p_k. The easiest way to see this is to use an inequality which is valid for any continuous convex function $\varphi(x)$

$$\varphi\Big(\frac{1}{n}\sum_{k=1}^{n} a_k\Big) \le \frac{1}{n}\sum_{k=1}^{n} \varphi(a_k),$$

where $a_1, a_2, \cdots, a_n$ are any positive numbers. Setting $a_k=p_k$ and $\varphi(x)=x \lg x$, and bearing in mind that $\sum_{k=1}^{n} p_k=1$, we find

$$\varphi\Big(\frac{1}{n}\Big)=\frac{1}{n} \lg \frac{1}{n} \le \frac{1}{n}\sum_{k=1}^{n} p_k \lg p_k = -\frac{1}{n}H(p_1, p_2, \cdots, p_n),$$

whence

$$H(p_1, p_2, \cdots, p_n) \le \lg n = H\Big(\frac{1}{n}, \frac{1}{n}, \cdots, \frac{1}{n}\Big), \quad \text{Q.E.D.}$$

Suppose now we have two finite schemes

$$A=\Big(\begin{matrix} A_1 & A_2 \cdots A_n \\ p_1 & p_2 \cdots p_n \end{matrix}\Big), \quad B=\Big(\begin{matrix} B_1 & B_2 \cdots B_m \\ q_1 & q_2 \cdots q_m \end{matrix}\Big),$$

and let these two schemes be (mutually) independent, i.e., the probability π_{kl} of the joint occurrence of the events A_k and B_l is $p_k q_l$. Then, the set of events $A_k B_l$ $(1 \le k \le n,\ 1 \le l \le m)$, with probabilities π_{kl} represents another finite scheme, which we call the *product* of the schemes A and B and designate by AB. Let $H(A)$, $H(B)$, and $H(AB)$ be the corresponding entropies of the schemes A, B, and AB. Then

$$H(AB)=H(A)+H(B), \qquad (2)$$

for, in fact

$$-H(AB)=\sum_k\sum_l \pi_{kl}\lg \pi_{kl}=\sum_k\sum_l p_k q_l (\lg p_k+\lg q_l)=$$
$$=\sum_k p_k \lg p_k \sum_l q_l+\sum_l q_l \lg q_l \sum_k p_k=-H(A)-H(B).$$

We now turn to the case where the schemes A and B are (mutually) dependent. We denote by q_{kl} the probability that the event B_l of the scheme B occurs, given that the event A_k of the scheme A occurred, so that

$$\pi_{kl}=p_k q_{kl} \ (1\leq k\leq n, \ 1\leq l\leq m).$$

Then

$$-H(AB)=\sum_k\sum_l p_k q_{kl} (\lg p_k+\lg q_{kl})=$$
$$=\sum_k p_k \lg p_k \sum_l q_{kl}+\sum_k p_k \sum_l q_{kl} \lg q_{kl}.$$

Here $\sum_l q_{kl}=1$ for any k, and the sum $-\sum_l q_{kl}\lg q_{kl}$ can be regarded as the conditional entropy $H_k(B)$ of the scheme B, calculated on the assumption that the event A_k of the scheme A occurred. We obtain

$$H(AB)=H(A)+\sum_k p_k H_k(B).$$

The conditional entropy $H_k(B)$ is obviously a random variable in the scheme A; its value is completely determined by the knowledge of which event A_k of the scheme A actually occurred. Therefore, the last term of the right side is the *mathematical expectation of the quantity* $H(B)$ *in the scheme* A, which we shall designate by $H_A(B)$. Thus in the most general case, we have

$$H(AB) = H(A) + H_A(B). \tag{3}$$

It is self-evident that the relation (3) reduces to (2) in the special case where the schemes A and B are independent.

It is also interesting to note that in all cases $H_A(B) \leq H(B)$. It is reasonable to interpret this inequality as saying that, on the average, knowledge of the outcome of the scheme A can only decrease the uncertainty of the scheme B. To prove this, we observe that any continuous convex function $f(x)$ obeys the inequality*

$$\sum_k \lambda_k f(x_k) \geq f(\sum_k \lambda_k x_k),$$

if $\lambda_k \geq 0$ and $\sum_k \lambda_k = 1$. Therefore, setting $f(x) = x \lg x$, $\lambda_k = p_k$, $x_k = q_{kl}$, we find for arbitrary l that

$$\sum_k p_k q_{kl} \lg q_{kl} \geq (\sum_k p_k q_{kl}) \lg (\sum_k p_k q_{kl}) = q_l \lg q_l,$$

since obviously $\sum_k p_k q_{kl} = q_l$. Summing over l, we obtain on the left side the quantity

$$\sum_k p_k \sum_l q_{kl} \lg q_{kl} = -\sum_k p_k H_k(B) = -H_A(B),$$

and consequently we find

$$-H_A(B) \geq \sum_l q_l \lg q_l = -H(B), \quad \text{Q.E.D.}$$

If we carry out an experiment the possible outcomes of which are described by the given scheme A, then in doing so we obtain some *information* (i.e., we find out which of the events

---

* See, for example, Hardy, Littlewood, and Pólya, *Inequalities*, Cambridge University Press, 1934.

A_k actually occurs), and the uncertainty of the scheme is completely eliminated. Thus, we can say that the information given us by carrying out some experiment consists in removing the uncertainty which existed before the experiment. The larger this uncertainty, the larger we consider to be the amount of information obtained by removing it. Since we agreed to measure the uncertainty of a finite scheme A by its entropy $H(A)$, it is natural to express the amount of information given by removing this uncertainty by an increasing function of the quantity $H(A)$. The choice of this function means the choice of some unit for the quantity of information and is therefore fundamentally a matter of indifference. However, the properties of entropy which we demonstrated above show that it is especially convenient to take this quantity of information proportional to the entropy. Indeed, consider two finite schemes A and B and their product AB. Realization of the scheme AB is obviously equivalent to realization of both of the schemes A and B. Therefore, if the two schemes A and B are independent, it is natural to require the information given by the realization of the scheme AB to be the sum of the two amounts of information given by the realization of the schemes A and B; since in this case

$$H(AB) = H(A) + H(B),$$

this requirement will actually be met, if we consider the amount of information given by the realization of a finite scheme to be proportional to the entropy of the scheme. Of course, the constant of proportionality can be taken as unity, since this choice corresponds merely to a choice of units. Thus, in all that follows, we can consider the amount of information given by the realization of a finite scheme to be equal to the entropy of the scheme. This stipulation makes the concept of entropy especially significant for information theory.

In view of this stipulation, let us consider the case of two dependent schemes A and B and the corresponding relation (3). The amount of information given by the realization of the scheme AB is equal to $H(AB)$. However, as explained above, in the general case, this cannot be equal to $H(A)+H(B)$. Indeed, consider the extreme case where knowledge of the outcome of the scheme A also determines with certainty the outcome of the scheme B, so that each event A_k of the scheme A can occur only in conjunction with a specific event B_l of the scheme B. Then, after realization of the scheme A, the scheme B completely loses its uncertainty, and we have $H_A(B)=0$; moreover, in this case realization of the scheme B obviously gives no further information, and we have $H(AB)=H(A)$, so that relation (3) is indeed satisfied. In all cases, the quantity $H_k(B)$ introduced above is the amount of information given by the scheme B, given that the event A_k occurred in the scheme A; therefore the quantity $H_A(B)=\sum_k p_k H_k(B)$ is the mathematical expectation of the amount of additional information given by realization of the scheme B after realization of scheme A and reception of the corresponding information. Therefore, the relation (3) has the following very reasonable interpretation: *The amount of information given by the realization of the two finite schemes A and B, equals the amount of information given by the realization of scheme A, plus the mathematical expectation of the amount of additional information given by the realization of scheme B after the realization of the scheme A.* In just the same way we can give an entirely reasonable interpretation of the general inequality $H_A(B) \leqq H(B)$ proved above: *The amount of information given by the realization of a scheme B can only decrease if another scheme A is realized beforehand.*

♯2. The Uniqueness Theorem

Among the properties of entropy which we have proved, we can consider the following two as basic:

1. For given n and for $\sum_{k=1}^{n} p_k = 1$, the function $H(p_1, p_2, \cdots, p_n)$ takes its largest value for $p_k = \dfrac{1}{n}$ $(k = 1, 2, \cdots, n)$.

2. $H(AB) = H(A) + H_A(B)$.

We add to these two properties a third, which obviously must be satisfied by any reasonable definition of entropy. Since the schemes

$$\begin{pmatrix} A_1 & A_2 & \cdots & A_n \\ p_1 & p_2 & \cdots & p_n \end{pmatrix} \text{ and } \begin{pmatrix} A_1 & A_2 & \cdots & A_n & A_{n+1} \\ p_1 & p_2 & \cdots & p_n & 0 \end{pmatrix},$$

are obviously not substantively different, we must have

3. $H(p_1, p_2, \cdots, p_n, 0) = H(p_1, p_2, \cdots, p_n)$. (Adding the impossible event or any number of impossible events to a scheme does not change its entropy.) We now prove the following important proposition:

Theorem 1.

Let $H(p_1, p_2, \cdots, p_n)$ be a function defined for any integer n and for all values $p_1, p_2, \cdots, p_n$ such that $p_k \geqq 0$ $(k = 1, 2, \cdots, n)$, $\sum_{k=1}^{n} p_k = 1$. If for any n this function is continuous with respect to all its arguments, and if it has the properties 1, 2, and 3, then

$$H(p_1, p_2, \cdots, p_n) = -\lambda \sum_{k=1}^{n} p_k \lg p_k,$$

where λ is a positive constant.

This theorem shows that the expression for the entropy of a finite scheme which we have chosen is the only one possible if we want it to have certain general properties which seem necessary in view of the actual meaning of the concept of entropy (as a measure of uncertainty or as an amount of information).

Proof.

For brevity we set

$$H\left(\frac{1}{n}, \frac{1}{n}, \cdots, \frac{1}{n}\right) = L(n);$$

we shall show that $L(n) = \lambda \lg n$, where λ is a positive constant. By 3 and 1, we have

$$L(n) = H\left(\frac{1}{n}, \frac{1}{n}, \cdots, \frac{1}{n}, 0\right) \leq H\left(\frac{1}{n+1}, \frac{1}{n+1}, \cdots, \frac{1}{n+1}\right) = L(n+1),$$

so that $L(n)$ is a non-decreasing function of n. Let m and r be positive integers. Consider m mutually independent finite schemes $S_1, S_2, \cdots, S_m$, each of which contains r equally likely events, so that

$$H(S_k) = H\left(\frac{1}{r}, \frac{1}{r}, \cdots, \frac{1}{r}\right) = L(r) \quad (1 \leq k \leq m).$$

By Property 2 (generalized to the case of m schemes) we have, in view of the independence of the schemes S_k

$$H(S_1 S_2 \cdots S_m) = \sum_{k=1}^{m} H(S_k) = mL(r).$$

But the product scheme $S_1 S_2 \cdots S_m$ obviously consists of r^m equally likely events, so that its entropy is $L(r^m)$. Therefore we have

$$L(r^m) = mL(r), \tag{4}$$

and similarly, for any other pair of positive integers n and s

$$L(s^n) = nL(s). \tag{5}$$

Now let the numbers r, s, and n be given arbitrarily, but let the number m be determined by the inequalities

$$r^m \leqq s^n \leqq r^{m+1}, \tag{6}$$

whence

$$m \lg r \leqq n \lg s < (m+1) \lg r,$$
$$\frac{m}{n} \leqq \frac{\lg s}{\lg r} < \frac{m}{n} + \frac{1}{n}. \tag{7}$$

It follows from (6) by the monotonicity of the function $L(n)$ that

$$L(r^m) \leqq L(s^n) \leqq L(r^{m+1}),$$

and, consequently, by (4) and (5)

$$mL(r) \leqq nL(s) \leqq (m+1)L(r),$$

so that

$$\frac{m}{n} \leqq \frac{L(s)}{L(r)} \leqq \frac{m}{n} + \frac{1}{n}. \tag{8}$$

Finally, it follows from (7) and (8) that

$$\left| \frac{L(s)}{L(r)} - \frac{\lg s}{\lg r} \right| \leqq \frac{1}{n}$$

Since the left side of this inequality is independent of m, and since n can be chosen arbitrarily large in the right side

$$\frac{L(s)}{\lg s} = \frac{L(r)}{\lg r},$$

which, in view of the arbitrariness of r and s, means that

$$L(n)=\lambda \lg n,$$

where λ is a constant. By the monotonicity of the function $L(n)$, we have $\lambda \geq 0$, and our assertion is proved.

This assertion represents the special case $p_k=1/n$ $(1 \leq k \leq n)$ of the theorem to be proved. We now consider the more general case, where the p_k $(k=1,2,\cdots,n)$ are any rational numbers. Let

$$p_k=\frac{g_k}{g} \quad (k=1,2,\cdots,n),$$

where all the g_k are positive integers and $\sum_{k=1}^{n} g_k=g$. Let the finite scheme A consist of n events with probabilities $p_1, p_2, \cdots, p_n$. Our problem consists in defining the entropy of this scheme. To this end, we consider a second scheme B, which is dependent on A and is defined as follows: The scheme B contains g events $B_1, B_2, \cdots, B_g$, which we devide into n groups, containing $g_1, g_2, \cdots, g_n$ events, respectively. If the event A_k occurred in scheme A, then in scheme B all the g_k events of the k'th group have the same probability $1/g_k$, and all the events of the other groups have probability zero (are impossible). Thus, given any outcome A_k of the scheme A, the scheme B reduces to a system of g_k equally likely events, so that the conditional entropy

$$H_k(B)=H(1/g_k, 1/g_k, \cdots, 1/g_k)=L(g_k)=\lambda \lg g_k,$$

which means that

$$H_A(B)=\sum_{k=1}^{n} p_k H_k(B)=\lambda \sum_{k=1}^{n} p_k \lg g_k=\lambda \sum_{k=1}^{n} p_k \lg p_k+\lambda \lg g. \quad (9)$$

We return now to the product scheme AB, consisting of the

events $A_k B_l$ $(1 \leq k \leq n,\ 1 \leq l \leq g)$. Such an event is possible only if B_l belongs to the k'th group. Thus, the number of possible events $A_k B_l$ for a given k is g_k, and the total number of possible events in the scheme AB is $\sum_{k=1}^{n} g_k = g$. The probability of each possible event $A_k B_l$ is obviously $p_k/g_k = 1/g$, i.e., is the same for all the events. Thus, the scheme AB consists of g equally likely events, and therefore

$$H(AB) = L(g) = \lambda \lg g.$$

Using property (2) and relation (9), we find

$$\lambda \lg g + H(A) + \lambda \sum_{k=1}^{n} p_k \lg p_k + \lambda \lg g,$$

whence

$$H(A) = H(p_1, p_2, \cdots, p_n) = -\lambda \sum_{k=1}^{n} p_k \lg p_k. \qquad (10)$$

Finally, relation (10) which we have proved for rational $p_1, p_2, \cdots, p_n$, must be valid for any values of its arguments because of the postulated continuity of the function $H(p_1, p_2, \cdots, p_n)$. Thus the proof of Theorem 1 is complete.

♯3. Entropy of Markov chains

Suppose we have a simple stationary Markov chain with a finite number of states $A_1, A_2, \cdots, A_n$ and with the transition probability matrix p_{ik} $(i, k = 1, 2, \cdots, n)$. We denote by P_k the probability of the state A_k $(1 \leq k \leq n)$, so that in particular

$$\sum_{k=1}^{} P_k p_{kl} = P_l \quad (l = 1, 2, \cdots, n). \qquad (11)$$

If the system is in state A_i, then its transitions to the different states A_k $(k = 1, 2, \cdots, n)$ form a finite scheme

$$\begin{pmatrix} A_1 & A_2 & \cdots & A_n \\ p_{i1} & p_{i2} & \cdots & p_{in} \end{pmatrix},$$

the entropy of which

$$H_i = -\sum_{k=1}^{n} p_{ik} \lg p_{ik}$$

depends on i and can be regarded as *a measure of the amount of information obtained when the Markov chain moves one step ahead, starting from the initial state* A_i. The average of this quantity over all initial states, i.e., the quantity

$$H = \sum_{i=1}^{n} P_i H_i = -\sum_{i=1}^{n} \sum_{k=1}^{n} P_i p_{ik} \lg p_{ik},$$

is therefore to be regarded as *a measure of the average amount of information obtained when the given Markov chain moves one step ahead.* This quantity H, which we shall call the *entropy* of the chain in question obviously characterizes the chain as a whole; it is clear that it is uniquely determined by giving the state probabilities P_i and the transition probabilities p_{ik} $(1 \leq i \leq n,\ 1 \leq k \leq n)$.

All the concepts which are defined for moving one step ahead can be easily and naturally generalized to the case of moving ahead an arbitrary number of steps r. If the system is in state A_i, then it is easy to calculate the probability that in the next r trials we shall find it in the states $A_{k_1}, A_{k_2}, \cdots, A_{k_r}$ in turn, where $k_1, k_2, \cdots, k_r$ are arbitrary numbers from 1 to n. Thus, the subsequent fate of a system initially in the state A_i in the next r trials is described by a finite scheme (with n^r events), with a definite entropy which we designate by H_i^r and regard as a measure of the amount of information obtained in moving ahead r steps in the chain, starting from the initial state A_i. The quantity

$$H^{(r)} = \sum_{i=1}^{n} P_i H_i^{(r)}$$

is to be regarded as the *average amount of information given by moving ahead r steps in the given Markov chain.* We shall call it the *r-step entropy* of the chain in question. The one-step entropy defined above can obviously be written as $H^{(1)}$.

If the notion of the quantity $H^{(r)}$ as the average amount of information obtained in moving ahead r steps in a given Markov chain is to be reasonable, then it is natural to require that for arbitrary positive integers r and s we have

$$H^{(r+s)} = H^{(r)} + H^{(s)},$$

or, equivalently, $H^{(r)} = rH^{(1)}$ for any positive integer r. It is easily seen that this is actually the case. In the first place, the relation $H^{(r)} = rH^{(1)}$ is trivially true for $r=1$. Suppose now that it is true for some $r \geq 1$; we shall show that in this case $H^{(r+1)} = (r+1)H^{(1)}$.

Let the system be in the state A_i; the finite scheme which escribes the fate of the system in the next $r+1$ trials, can hen be regarded as the product of two dependent schemes:

A) the scheme corresponding to the immediately following rial with the entropy $H_i^{(1)}$ and

B) the scheme describing the fate of the system in the next r trials; the entropy of this scheme is $H_k^{(r)}$, if the outcome of scheme A was the event A_k. According to the general relation

$$H(AB) = H(A) + H_A(B),$$

we have

$$H_i^{(r+1)} = H_i^{(1)} + \sum_{k=1}^{n} p_{ik} H_k^{(r)},$$

and consequently, in view of (11)

$$H^{(r+1)} = \sum_{i=1}^{n} P_i H_i^{(r+1)} = \sum_{i=1}^{n} P_i H_i^{(1)} + \sum_{k=1}^{n} H_k^{(r)} \sum_{i=1}^{n} P_i p_{ik} =$$

$$= H^{(1)} + \sum_{k=1}^{n} P_k H_k^{(r)} = H^{(1)} + H^{(r)} = (r+1)H^{(1)}, \quad \text{Q.E.D.}$$

In a large number of cases, the application of the concept of the entropy of Markov chains in information theory is based on two fundamental theorems, which we shall prove in the next section.

#4.   Fundamental Theorems

Suppose now that the Markov chain we are studying obeys the law of large numbers, i.e. that in a sufficiently long sequence of s consecutive trials the relative frequency $\dfrac{m_i}{s}$ of occurrence of the state A_i will differ from P_i by an arbitrarily small amount, with a probability arbitrarily close to unity. In other words, for arbitrarily small $\varepsilon > 0$ and $\delta > 0$, and for sufficiently large s

$$P\left\{ \frac{m_i}{s} - P_i > \delta \right\} < \varepsilon^{*)}. \qquad (12)$$

For brevity, we shall call such a chain *ergodic*.

Each possible result of the series of s consecutive trials of the given Markov chain can be written as a "sequence"

$$A_{k_1}, A_{k_2}, \cdots, A_{k_s}, \qquad (C)$$

where $k_1, k_2, \cdots, k_s$ are numbers from 1 to n. The probability of realizing the sequence (C) does not depend on the part of the chain where the series of trials begins (because of the

---

*) A. A. Markov showed that for this to be the case it is sufficient to assume that the chain in question is "transitive", i.e., that a transition is possible from any state to any other state in a sufficiently large number of steps. For the chains with which information theory is concerned, this hypothesis is apparently always fulfilled.

stationarity), and is obviously equal to

$$p(C)=P_{k_1}p_{k_1k_2}p_{k_2k_3}\cdots p_{k_{s-1}k_s}.$$

Let i and l be two arbitrary numbers from 1 to n, and let m_{il} be the number of pairs of the form k_rk_{r+1} $(1\leq r\leq s)$ in which $k_r=i$, $k_{r+1}=l$. Then, clearly the probability of the sequence (C) can be written in the form

$$p(C)=P_{k_1}\prod_{i=1}^{n}\prod_{l=1}^{n}(p_{il})^{m_{il}}. \tag{13}$$

Theorem 2.

Given $\varepsilon>0$ and $\eta>0$, no matter how small, for sufficiently large n all sequences of the form (C) can be divided into two groups with the following properties: 1) the probability $p(C)$ of any sequence of the first group satisfies the inequality

$$\left|\frac{\lg\dfrac{1}{p(C)}}{s}-H\right|<\eta, \tag{14}$$

and 2) the sum of the probabilities of all sequences of the second group is less than ε.

In other words, all sequences with the exception of a very low probability group have probabilities lying between $a^{-s(H+\eta)}$ and $a^{-s(H-\eta)}$, where a is the base of the system of logarithms used. Here H is the one-step entropy of the given chain.

Proof.

We shall agree to assign the sequence (C) to the first group if it has the following two properties:

1. it is a possible outcome, i.e. $p(C)>0$, and
2. for any i, l $(1\leq i\leq n,\ 1\leq l\leq n)$ the inequality

$$|m_{il}-sP_ip_{il}| < s\delta \tag{15}$$

obtains. All the other sequences are assigned to the second group. We shall show that this division satisfies both requirements of theorem 2, if $\delta > 0$ is sufficiently small and if s is sufficiently large.

1) Suppose the sequence (C) belongs to the first group. It follows from (15) that

$$m_{il}=sP_ip_{il}+s\delta\theta_{il}, \ |\theta_{il}|<1, \ 1\leq i\leq n, \ 1\leq l\leq n.$$

We now substitute these expressions for the numbers m_{il} in (13), where in doing so we must bear in mind that the requirement that the given sequence be a possible outcome implies that $m_{il}=0$ when $p_{il}=0$. Thus in the product (13) we must restrict ourselves to factors such that $p_{il}>0$, which we shall denote by an asterisk on the product signs. We find

$$p(C)=P_{k_1}\prod_i\prod_l{}^*(p_{il})^{sP_ip_{il}+s\delta\theta_{il}},$$

$$\lg\frac{1}{p(C)}=-\lg P_{k_1}-s\sum_i\sum_l{}^* P_ip_{il}\lg p_{il}-s\delta\sum_i\sum_l{}^*\theta_{il}\lg p_{il}=$$

$$=-\lg P_{k_1}+sH-s\delta\sum_i\sum_l{}^*\theta_{il}\lg p_{il},$$

whence

$$\left|\frac{\lg\dfrac{1}{p(C)}}{s}-H\right|<\frac{1}{s}\lg\frac{1}{P_{k_1}}+\delta\sum_i\sum_l{}^*\lg\frac{1}{p_{il}}.$$

This means that for sufficiently large s

$$\left|\frac{\lg\dfrac{1}{p(C)}}{s}-H\right|<\eta,$$

where $\eta>0$ is as small as we please if δ is sufficiently small.

Thus, the first requirement of Theorem 2 is satisfied.

2) Turning now to the calculation of the sum of the probabilities of all the sequences of the second group, we note first of all that the impossible sequences in this group are not included in this calculation, since their probabilities are zero. Thus, we only have to calculate the sum of the probabilities of those sequences for which the inequality (15) does not hold for at least one pair of indices i, l; to do this it suffices to calculate the quantity

$$\sum_{i=1}^{n} \sum_{l=1}^{n} P\{|m_{il} - sP_i p_{il}| \geqq s\delta\}.$$

First we fix the indices i and l. By (12) we have for sufficiently large s

$$P\left\{|m_i - sP_i| < \frac{\delta}{2}s\right\} > 1 - \varepsilon.$$

If the inequality $\{\ \}$ is satisfied, and if s is sufficiently large, then m_i is as large as we please, and therefore by Bernouilli's theorem

$$P\left\{\left|\frac{m_{il}}{m_i} - p_{il}\right| < \frac{\delta}{2}\right\} > 1 - \varepsilon.$$

Therefore the probability of satisfying both of the inequalities

$$|m_i - sP_i| < \frac{\delta}{2}s, \tag{16}$$

$$|m_{il} - m_i p_{il}| < \frac{\delta}{2}m_{il} \leqq \frac{\delta}{2}s \tag{17}$$

exceeds $(1-\varepsilon)^2 > 1 - 2\varepsilon$. But it follows from (16) that

$$|p_{il}m_i - sP_i p_{il}| < p_{il}\frac{\delta}{2}s < \frac{\delta}{2}s,$$

and this together with (17) gives

$$|m_{il} - sP_ip_{il}| < \delta s. \tag{18}$$

Thus for any i and l, we have for sufficiently large s

$$P\{|m_{il} - sP_ip_{il}| < \delta s\} > 1 - 2\varepsilon,$$

which means that

$$P\{|m_{il} - sP_ip_{il}| > \delta s\} < 2\varepsilon.$$

From this it follows that

$$\sum_{i=1}^{n}\sum_{l=1}^{n} P\{|m_{il} - sP_ip_{il}| > \delta s\} < 2n^2\varepsilon.$$

Since the right side of this inequality is together with ε arbitrarily small, the sum of the probabilities of all the sequences of the second group can be made as small as we please for sufficiently large s, i.e., the second requirement of Theorem 2 is also satisfied. Thus Theorem 2 is proved.

We now note that the number of all s-term sequences of the form (C) equals n^s, and we arrange these sequences in order of decreasing probability $p(C)$. We select sequences from this series in the order in which we have arranged them until the sum of the probabilities of the sequences selected just exceeds a preassigned positive number λ $(0 < \lambda < 1)$. We denote by $N_s(\lambda)$ the number of sequences so selected. Theorem 2 permits us to make the following important estimate of the number $N_s(\lambda)$.

Theorem 3. $\lim\limits_{s \to \infty} \dfrac{\lg N_s(\lambda)}{s} = H.$

In particular, the indicated limit does not depend on the number λ, if only $0 < \lambda < 1$ and λ remains constant as s increases.

Proof.

We agree to call a sequence (C) *standard* if its probability $p(C)$ satisfies the inequality (14) where η is a fixed, arbitrarily small positive number. By Theorem 2, the sum of the probabilities of all non-standard sequences is arbitrarily small for sufficiently large s. The inequality (14) is equivalent to the inequality.

$$a^{-s(H+\eta)} < p(C) < a^{-s(H-\eta)}, \tag{19}$$

which therefore are characteristic of standard sequences (a denotes the base of the system of logarithms used).

The following sequences are among the selected sequences (with sum of probabilities $> \lambda$):

1) all non-standard sequences with probabilities $p(C) \geq a^{-s(H-\eta)}$; the sum of the probabilities of such seqences does not exceed the sum of the probabilities of *all* non-standard sequences, which latter is for sufficiently large s less than any $\varepsilon > 0$, however small.

2) a certain number $M_s(\lambda)$ of standard sequences, the sum of the probabilities of which must be greater than $\lambda - \varepsilon$ (since the sum of the probabilities of the selected sequences exceeds λ).

The non-standard sequences with probabilities $p(C) \leq a^{-s(H+\eta)}$ can not be among the selected sequences, since according to Theorem 2 the sum of the probabilities of the standard sequences by themselves exceeds λ. Thus, for all the selected sequences $p(C) > a^{-s(H+\eta)}$, and therefore the sum of the probabilities of the selected sequences is greater than $N_s(\lambda) a^{-s(H+\eta)}$. On the other hand, this sum is obviously less than $\lambda + q$, where q is the probability of the last sequence selected; thus

$$N_s(\lambda) a^{-s(H+\eta)} < \lambda + q < \lambda + a^{-s(H-\eta)},$$

which means (since $\lambda < 1$) that for sufficiently large s

$$N_s(\lambda)a^{-s(H+\eta)} < 1,$$

whence

$$\frac{\lg N_s(\lambda)}{s} < H + \eta. \tag{20}$$

On the other hand, the $M_s(\lambda)$ standard sequences which we have selected have probabilities $p(C) < a^{-s(H-\eta)}$, while their sum is larger than $\lambda - \varepsilon$. It follows that

$$M_s(\lambda)a^{-s(H-\eta)} > \lambda - \varepsilon,$$

so that *a fortiori*

$$N_s(\lambda)a^{-s(H-\eta)} > \lambda - \varepsilon,$$

whence

$$\frac{\lg N_s(\lambda)}{s} > H - \eta + \frac{1}{s}\lg(\lambda - \varepsilon). \tag{21}$$

Combining the inequalities (20) and (21) obviously proves Theorem 3, since the number η can be made arbitrarily small for sufficiently large s.

The great value of Theorem 3 for a variety of applications depends on the following considerations. Whereas the number of sequences of type (C) is $n^s = a^{s\lg n}$, the number $N_s(\lambda)$ of selected sequences is approximately a^{sH}, as Theorem 3 shows. If we recall that $\lg n$ is the maximum value of the entropy H and that, consequently, we always have $H < \lg n$ (except for a trivial case) and if we choose the number λ very close to unity, then Theorem 3 shows that a negligibly small fraction of all the sequences (C) has a sum of probabilities arbitrarily close to unity (for sufficiently large s). Moreover, we see that the *entropy* of the given Markov chain plays a decisive role in determining *how small* this fraction is.

♯5   Application to Coding Theory

In order to give at least one example which illustrates the practical applications of the entropy concept, we now consider one of the simplest problems of coding theory. Suppose that the text which is to be coded consists of a sequence of symbols (letters) belonging to a finite set (alphabet), and denote by m the number of different symbols (so that the number of different sequences of length s is m^s). We shall regard this text as a simple Markov chain of the type considered in the two preceding sections and assume that its statistical structure is known, in particular its entropy H. (We know that the maximum value of H is $\lg m$.) We restrict ourselves to a consideration of the simplest case where the text at hand is coded *into the same alphabet*, i.e., each sequence from the text is coded into a sequence of letters from the same alphabet. (Actually, of course, it is only important that the coded text has the same *number* of symbols as the uncoded text, since no role is played by the designation of the symbols.) It goes without saying that the rules of coding must guarantee that the original text can be uniquely reconstructed from the coded text, which requires in particular that different sequences of the uncoded text must be coded differently.

It is immediately clear that by using as short a coding as possible for the most commonly encountered sequences, and conversely, by leaving the longer coding for the more rarely encountered sequences, we have the possibility of making the coded text shorter than the original, which obviously might constitute a practical and economic advantage. In order to analyze this possibility, we must first of all choose quantities which can measure in a natural way this kind of compression by coding. It is apparent at once that both the possible amount of compression and the choice of an optimum code to achieve it depend entirely on the statistical structure of the given text.

Each s-term sequence (C) of symbols from the input text has a definite probability $p(C)$, and the sequence of coded text into which it is transformed by the coding has a definite length $\sigma(C)$. The ratio $\sigma(C)/s$ can be regarded as a "compression coefficient" for the given s-term sequence. The mathematical expectation of this ratio

$$\mu_s = \frac{\sum_C p(C)\sigma(C)}{s}$$

(where the summation is over all sequences of length s) is the "average compression" for sequences of length s; finally, the quantity

$$\mu = \varlimsup_{s \to \infty} \mu_s$$

which we shall call the *compression coefficient* (of a given text for a given code) can clearly serve to measure in a natural way the compression of the given uncoded text by the given means of coding. In addition, we note that in all cases actually encountered the quantity μ_s approaches a definite limit as $s \to \infty$.

We are interested in the smallest value of the compression coefficient that can be achieved by coding when the text has a given statistical structure. Naturally, at the same time we are interested in how to construct the corresponding "optimum" code. A complete answer to these questions is contained in the following remarkably simple theorem:

Theorem 4.

If the entropy of the given text is H, then the greatest lower bound of the compression coefficient μ for all possible codes is $H/\lg m$, where m is the number of different symbols of the text.

Thus, to find the greatest lower bound of the possible shortening of a text by coding, there is no need to know in detail the statistical structure of the text; it is sufficient to consider only its entropy and the number of symbols it uses. Since $\lg m$ is the maximum value of H for the given number of symbols, the quantity $H/\lg m$ is sometimes called the "relative entropy" of the given text.

Proof.

We must show that 1) for any code $\mu \geq \dfrac{H}{\lg m}$ and 2) for arbitrarily small $\eta > 0$, there exists a code for which $\mu < \dfrac{H+\eta}{\lg m}$.

1) Choose an arbitrary code and let $H' = H - 2\eta$, where $\eta > 0$ is arbitrarily small. We agree to call an s-term sequence of the given text a *special* sequence, if $\sigma(C) < H's/\lg m$. Since the number of different k-term sequences of the coded text is m^k, the number of all special s-term sequences of the text is no greater than

$$m + m^2 + \cdots + m^{\left\lfloor \frac{H's}{\lg m} \right\rfloor} \leq m^{\frac{H's}{\lg m}} \left\{ 1 + \frac{1}{m} + \frac{1}{m^2} + \cdots \right\} = \frac{m}{m-1} \, a^{sH'},$$

where a is the base of the system of logarithms used. We shall denote the sum of the probabilities of all the special sequences by λ_s and show that $\lambda_s \to 0$ as $s \to \infty$.

In fact, let $\varepsilon > 0$ be an arbitrarily small constant; then, by Theorem 3, to obtain a sum of probabilities equal to ε, we must take

$$N_s(\varepsilon) > a^{s(H-\eta)} = a^{s(H'+\eta)}$$

of the most probable sequences. But, as we have seen, for sufficiently large s, the number of all special sequences does not exceed

$$\frac{m}{m-1} a^{sH'} < a^{s(H'+\eta)}.$$

Therefore, the sum λ_s of these probabilities is less than ε if s is sufficiently large, i.e., $\lambda_s \to 0$ as $s \to \infty$, as was to be shown.

Since for every non-special sequence (C)

$$\sigma(C) \geqq \frac{H's}{\lg m},$$

the mathematical expectation of $\sigma(C)$ exceeds $(1-\lambda_s)\dfrac{H's}{\lg m}$, and therefore

$$\mu_s \geqq (1-\lambda_s)\frac{H'}{\lg m},$$

but since $\lambda_s \to 0$ as $s \to \infty$

$$\mu = \varlimsup_{s \to \infty} \mu_s \geqq \frac{H'}{\lg m} = \frac{H-2\eta}{\lg m}.$$

Finally, since η is arbitrarily small, we have

$$\mu \geqq \frac{H}{\lg m},$$

which proves the first assertion of Theorem 4.

2) Let $\eta > 0$ be arbitrarily small; to prove the second assertion of Theorem 4, we determine directly a code for which $\mu < \dfrac{H+\eta}{\lg m}$. Let $\delta > 0$ be arbitrarily small. The number of different sequences of lenth $\dfrac{s(H+\delta)}{\lg m}$ equals

$$m^{\frac{s(H+\delta)}{\lg m}} = a^{s(H+\delta)}.$$

In addition, let $\varepsilon > 0$ be arbitrarily small: by Theorem 3, the number $N_s(1-\varepsilon)$ of most probable s-term sequences the sum of which has probability greater than or equal to $1-\varepsilon$ is less than $a^{s(H+\delta)}$, if s is sufficiently large. Therefore, all these "high-probability" s-term sequences can be coded using sequences of length $\dfrac{s(H+\delta)}{\lg m}$, since, as we see, there are enough of the latter to do so. As regards the remaining "low-probability" s-term sequences (with total probability less than ε), we simply code each of them into itself. In order to guarantee uniqueness of decoding, it is sufficient (for example) to put one of the previously unused sequences of length $\dfrac{s(H+\delta)}{\lg m}$ (but always the same one!) in front of each such s-term sequence of the coded text. For a code chosen in this way, the length $\sigma(C)$ of a coded s-term sequence will be either $\dfrac{s(H+\delta)}{\lg m}$ or $s + \dfrac{s(H+\delta)}{\lg m}$, where the first eventuality occurs with a probability less than or equal to unity and the second with a probability less than or equal to ε. Therefore, the mathematical expectation of $\sigma(C)$ does not exceed

$$\frac{s(H+\delta)}{\lg m} + \varepsilon\left[s + \frac{s(H+\delta)}{\lg m} \right] = s\left[\frac{H+\delta}{\lg m}(1+\varepsilon) + \varepsilon \right] < s\,\frac{H+\eta}{\lg m},$$

if ε and δ are chosen sufficiently small.

Suppose now we have a large text (C) of length $S = ks$, where k is very large. This text can be broken up into k sequences $C_1, C_2, \cdots, C_k$ of length s; correspondingly, the coded text of length $\sigma(C)$ falls into k sequences with corresponding lengths $\sigma(C_1), \sigma(C_2), \cdots \sigma(C_k)$, so that

$$\sigma(C) = \sigma(C_1) + \sigma(C_2) + \cdots + \sigma(C_k).$$

Therefore, the mathematical expectation of $\sigma(C)$ is k times the mathematical expectation of the quantity $\sigma(C_1)$, and so by the foregoing, does not exceed

$$ks\left(\frac{H+\eta}{\lg m}\right) = S\,\frac{H+\eta}{\lg m}.$$

It follows that

$$\mu_s \leq \frac{H+\eta}{\lg m},$$

and consequently that

$$\mu \leq \frac{H+\eta}{\lg m},$$

which proves the second assertion of Theorem 4.

(Translated by R. A. Silverman)

On the Fundamental Theorems of
Information Theory

On the Fundamental Theorems of Information Theory

(Uspekhi Matematicheskikh Nauk, vol. XI, no. 1, 1956, pp. 17–75)

INTRODUCTION

Information theory is one of the youngest branches of applied probability theory; it is not yet ten years old. The date of its birth can, with certainty, be considered to be the appearance in 1947–1948 of the by now classical work of Claude Shannon [1]. Rarely does it happen in mathematics that a new discipline achieves the character of a mature and developed scientific theory in the first investigation devoted to it. Such in its time was the case with the theory of integral equations, after the fundamental work of Fredholm; so it was with information theory after the work of Shannon.

From the very beginning, information theory presents mathematics with a whole new set of problems, including some very difficult ones. It is quite natural that Shannon and his first disciples, whose basic goal was to obtain practical results, were not able to pay enough attention to these mathematical difficulties at the beginning. Consequently, at many points of their investigations they were compelled either to be satisfied with reasoning of an inconclusive nature or to limit artificially the set of objects studied' (sources, channels, codes, etc.) in order to simplify the proofs. Thus, the whole mass of literature of the first years of information theory, of necessity, bears the imprint of mathematical incompleteness which, in particular, makes it extremely difficult for mathematicians to become acquainted with this new subject. The recently published general textbook on information theory by S. Goldman [2] can serve as a typical example of the style prevalent in this literature.

Investigations, with the aim of setting information theory on a solid mathematical basis have begun to appear only in recent years and, at the present time, are few in number. First of all, we must mention the work of McMillan [3] in which the fundamental concepts of the theory of discrete sources (source, channel, code, etc.) were first given precise mathematical definitions. The most important result of this work must be considered to be the proof of the remarkable theorem that any discrete ergodic source has the property which Shannon attributed to sources of Markov type and which underlies almost all the asymptotic calculations of information theory.* This circumstance permits the whole theory of discrete information to be constructed without being limited, as was Shannon, to Markov type sources. In the rest of his paper McMillan tries to put Shannon's fundamental theorem on channels with noise on a rigorous basis. In doing so, it becomes apparent that the sketchy proof given by Shannon contains gaps which remain even in the case of Markov sources. The elimination of these gaps is begun in McMillan's paper, but is not completed.

Next, it is necessary to mention the work of Feinstein [4]. Like McMillan, Feinstein considers the Shannon theorem on channels with noise to be the pinnacle of the general theory of discrete information and he undertakes to give a mathematically rigorous proof of this theorem. Accepting completely McMillan's mathematical apparatus, he avoids following Shannon's original path and constructs a proof, using the completely new and apparently very fruitful idea of a " distinguishable set of sequences ", the principal features of which will be explained below. However, Feinstein carries out the proof in

---

* Sections 5-8 of this paper are devoted to this theorem.

all details only for the simplest and least practical case, where the successive signals of the source are mutually independent and the channel memory is zero. In the more general case, he indicates only sketchily how the reader is to carry out the necessary reasoning independently. Unfortunately, there remains a whole series of significant difficulties.

As is well known, Shannon formulated his theorem on channels with noise in two different ways. One was in terms of a quantity called *equivocation*, and the other was in terms of the *probability of error*. McMillan's analysis leads to the conclusion that these two formulations are not equivalent, and that the second gives a more exact result than the first. Feinstein's more detailed investigation showed that although the first formulation is implied by the second, a rigorous derivation of this implication is not only non-trivial but fraught with considerable additional difficulties. Since both formulations are equally important in actual content, it is preferable to speak about two Shannon theorems rather than combine them under the same heading.

In this paper I attempt to give a complete, detailed proof of both of these Shannon theorems, assuming any ergodic source and any stationary channel with a finite memory. At the present time, apparently, these are the broadest hypotheses under which the Shannon theorems can be regarded as valid. On the whole, I follow the path indicated in the works of McMillan and Feinstein, deviating from them only in the comparatively few cases when I see a gap in their explanation, or when another explanation seems to me more complete and convincing (and sometimes, more simple).

The first chapter of the paper, which is of purely auxiliary character, requires special explanation. It is devoted to the derivation of a whole set of unrelated inequalities, each of which is a theorem of elementary probability theory (i. e., pertains only to finite spaces). The reader acquainted with my paper [5] will be able to begin this paper with the second chapter, returning to the first chapter only when references to its results appear in the text. All the following chapters are constructed according to a specific plan, and can not be skipped or read in different order.

The reader will see that the path to the Shannon theorems is long and thorny, but apparently science, at this time, knows no shorter path if we do not want artificial restrictions on the material studied and if we are to avoid making statements which we can not prove.

CHAPTER I.

Elementary Inequalities

#1. Two generalizations of Shannon's inequality

Let A be a finite probability space composed of elementary events A_i with probabilities

$$p(A_i)\ (1 \leq i \leq n,\ p(A_i) > 0\ ;\ \sum_{i=1}^{n} p(A_i) = 1).$$

The quantity*

$$H(A) = -\sum_{i=1}^{n} p(A_i) \lg p(A_i)$$

is called the *entropy* of the space A. The significance of this quantity as a measure of uncertainty or as the amount of information contained in the space A was illustrated by us in detail in [5]. Important properties of the entropy are enumerated there.

Let us now consider, along with A, another finite space B, with the elementary events B_k and the distribution $p(B_k)\ (1 \leq k \leq m,\ p(B_k) > 0\ ;\ \sum_{k=1}^{m} p(B_k) = 1)$. The events A_i and B_k of the spaces A and B can be dependent. The events $A_i B_k$ with the probabilities $p(A_i B_k)$ can be regarded as elementary events of a new finite space which we shall designate by AB (or BA), and which we shall call the *product* of the spaces A and B. The entropy of this space is

$$H(AB) = -\sum_{i=1}^{n} \sum_{k=1}^{m} p(A_i B_k) \lg p(A_i B_k).$$

If it is known that the event A_i occurred, then the events B_k

---

* In this paper all logarithms are to the base 2.

of the space B have the new probabilities

$$p_{A_i}(B_k) = \frac{p(A_i B_k)}{p(A_i)} \qquad (k = 1, 2, \cdots, m)$$

instead of the previous $p(B_k)$. Correspondingly, the previous entropy of the space B

$$H(B) = -\sum_{k=1}^{m} p(B_k) \lg p(B_k)$$

is replaced by the new quantity

$$H_{A_i}(B) = -\sum_{k=1}^{m} p_{A_i}(B_k) \lg p_{A_i}(B_k),$$

which, naturally, we shall regard as the conditional entropy of the space B under the assumption that the event A_i occurred in the space A. A specific value of $H_{A_i}(B)$ corresponds to each of the events A_i of the space A, so that $H_{A_i}(B)$ can be regarded as a random variable defined on the space A. The mathematical expectation of this random variable

$$H_A(B) = \sum_{i=1}^{m} p(A_i) H_{A_i}(B)$$

is the conditional entropy of the space B averaged over the space A. It indicates how much information is contained on the average in the space B, if it is known which of the events of the space A actually occurred. In my paper [5], it is shown that

(1.1) $$H(AB) = H(A) + H_A(B),$$

a relation which is very natural from the standpoint of the real meaning of the quantities in it; in the special case where the spaces A and B are (mutually) independent, we have $H_A(B) = H(B)$, and therefore

$$H(AB) = H(A) + H(B).$$

Shannon's fundamental inequality (also introduced in my paper) is especially important for the purposes of this section. It states that for any finite spaces A and B

(1.2) $$H_A(B) \leq H(B),$$

the real meaning of which is that, on the average, the amount of uncertainty in the space B can either decrease or remain the same, if it is known which event occurred in some other space A. (The uncertainty of a situation can not be increased as a result of obtaining any additional information.) It follows from (1.1) and (1.2) that

(1.3) $$H(AB) \leq H(A) + H(B),$$

an inequality which is easily generalized to the case of the product of any number of spaces; thus

$$H(ABC) \leq H(A) + H(B) + H(C),$$

etc. The inequality (1.2) can be generalized in various directions; we now prove two such generalizations, which will be needed subsequently.

Let A and B be any two finite spaces. We keep all the notation introduced above. In expanded form, (1.2) becomes

$$\sum_{i=1}^{n} p(A_i) \sum_{k=1}^{m} p_{A_i}(B_k) \lg p_{A_i}(B_k) \geq \sum_{k=1}^{m} p(B_k) \lg p(B_k).$$

For later use, it is important to show that this inequality remains valid when we sum both sides not over all, but only over certain values of the subscript k (but, of course, over the same values in both sides of the inequality). In other words, this inequality does not depend on whether or not the events B_k form a "complete system".

Lemma 1.1.

(1.4) $\sum_{i=1}^{n} p(A_i) \sum_k^* p_{A_i}(B_k) \lg p_{A_i}(B_k) \geqq \sum_k^* p(B_k) \lg p(B_k),$

where $\sum_k^*$ denotes summation over certain values of the subscript k (not necessarily all, but the same values in both sides of the inequality).

Remark.

In the special case where the summation is carried out over all k $(1 \leqq k \leqq m)$, the left and right sides of (1.4) become $-H_A(B)$ and $-H(B)$, respectively, so that (1.4) agrees with (1.2). Therefore, (1.2) is a special case of Lemma 1.1, and hence is proved when it is.

Proof.

The function $f(x) = x \lg x$ is convex for $x > 0$; consequently, for $x_i > 0$, $\lambda_i \geqq 0$, $\sum_{i=1}^{n} \lambda_i = 1$, the following inequality holds (see [5], [6])

(1.5) $\sum_{i=1}^{n} \lambda_i f(x_i) \geqq f\left(\sum_{i=1}^{n} \lambda_i x_i \right).$

Putting $\lambda_i = p(A_i)$, $x_i = p_{A_i}(B_k)$, we find

$$\sum_{i=1}^{n} p(A_i) \sum_k^* p_{A_i}(B_k) \lg p_{A_i}(B_k) = \sum_k^* \left\{ \sum_{i=1}^{n} p(A_i) f[p_{A_i}(B_k)] \right\}$$

$$\geqq \sum_k^* f\left\{ \sum_{i=1}^{n} p(A_i) p_{A_i}(B_k) \right\} = \sum_k^* f[p(B_k)] = \sum_k^* p(B_k) \lg p(B_k), \text{ Q.E.D.}$$

Now we generalize the inequality (1.2) in another direction.

Lemma 1.2.

For any three finite spaces A, B, C

$$H_{AB}(C) \leqq H_B(C).$$

Remark.

In the special case where the space B consists of one event with probability 1, the space AB coincides with A, and $H_B(C) = H(C)$. For this special case, the statement of Lemma 1.2 becomes

$$H_A(C) \leqq H(C),$$

and is equivalent to the inequality (1.2), which is therefore a special case of Lemma 1.1.

Proof.

Let a given event B_k occur in the space B; then all the events $A_i C_l$ in the product space AC have the probabilities $p_{B_k}(A_i C_l) = q(A_i C_l)$; in just the same way the space A becomes the space A' with the probabilities $p_{B_k}(A_i) = q(A_i)$ and the space C becomes C' with the probabilities $p_{B_k}(C_l) = q(C_l)$. Hence, according to inequality (1.2)

(1.6) $$H_{A'}(C') \leqq H(C').$$

But

(1.7) $$H(C') = -\sum_i q(C_l) \lg q(C_l) = -\sum p_{B_k}(C_l) \lg p_{B_k}(C_l) = H_{B_k}(C).$$

On the other hand

$$H_{A'}(C') = -\sum_i q(A_i) \sum q_{A_i}(C_l) \lg q_{A_i}(C_l),$$

where

$$q_{A_i}(C_l) = \frac{q(A_i C_l)}{q(A_i)} = \frac{p_{B_k}(A_i C_l)}{p_{B_k}(A_i)} = p_{B_k A_i}(C_l);$$

consequently

(1.8) $$H_{A'}(C') = -\sum_i p_{B_k}(A_i) \sum_l p_{B_k A_i}(C_l) \lg p_{B_k A_i}(C_l)$$

$$= \sum_i p_{B_k}(A_i) H_{B_k A_i}(C).$$

Substituting (1.7) and (1.8) into (1.6), we find

$$\sum_i p_{B_k}(A_i) H_{B_k A_i}(C) \leqq H_{B_k}(C).$$

Multiplying both sides of this inequality by $p(B_k)$ and then summing over all k, we obtain

$$\sum_{i,k} p(B_k) p_{B_k}(A_i) H_{B_k A_i}(C) \leqq \sum_k p(B_k) H_{B_k}(C),$$

or

$$\sum_{i,k} p(A_i B_k) H_{A_i B_k}(C) \leqq H_B(C),$$

or, finally

$$H_{AB}(C) \leqq H_B(C), \qquad \text{Q. E. D.}$$

$\sharp 2.$ Three Inequalities of Feinstein [4]

We again consider two finite spaces A and B and their product AB. Let Z be some set of events $A_i B_k$ of the space AB, and let U_0 be some set of events A_i of the space A; let $\delta_1 > 0$, $\delta_2 > 0$, and

$$p(Z) > 1 - \delta_1; \qquad p(U_0) > 1 - \delta_2.$$

Let us denote by Γ_i $(1 \leqq i \leqq n)$ the set of events B_k of the space B for which $A_i B_k$ does not being to the set Z. Finally, let U_1 be the set of events $A_i \in U_0$ for which $p_{A_i}(\Gamma_i) \leqq \alpha$. Then we have

Lemma 2.1.

$$p(U_1) > 1 - \delta_2 - \frac{\delta_1}{\alpha}.$$

Proof.

Let U_2 be the set of events A_i for which $p_{A_i}(\Gamma_i) > \alpha$, so that

$$(2.1) \qquad\qquad U_1 = U_0 - U_0 U_2.$$

If $A_i \in U_2$, then

$$p(A_i \Gamma_i) = p(A_i) p_{A_i}(\Gamma_i) > \alpha p(A_i),$$

which means that

$$p\left(\sum_{A_i \in U_2} A_i \Gamma_i \right) = \sum_{A_i \in U_2} p(A_i \Gamma_i) > \alpha \sum_{A_i \in U_2} p(A_i) = \alpha p(U_2).$$

On the other hand, since all the events $A_i \Gamma_i$ are incompatible with the event Z, the probability of which exceeds $1 - \delta_1$, then

$$p\left(\sum_{A_i \in U_2} A_i \Gamma_i \right) \leq 1 - p(Z) < \delta_1,$$

and we find that $\alpha p(U_2) < \delta_1$, or $p(U_2) < \delta_1/\alpha$. It follows, *a fortiori*, that

$$p(U_0 U_2) < \frac{\delta_1}{\alpha};$$

hence, by (2.1)

$$p(U_1) = p(U_0) - p(U_0 U_2) > 1 - \delta_2 - \delta_1/\alpha, \qquad \text{Q. E. D.}$$

For a given subscript k $(1 \leq k \leq m)$, we now designate by i_k the value of the subscript i $(1 \leq i \leq n)$, for which the probability $p(A_i B_k)$ assumes its greatest value (in the space AB); if there is more than one such i value, we take any one as i_k. Thus A_{i_k} is the event of the space A which is most probable for a given event B_k of the space B. Obviously, the sum

$$P = \sum_{k=1}^{m} \sum_{\substack{i=1 \\ i \neq i_k}}^{n} p(A_i B_k)$$

is the probability (in the space AB) of the appearance of a pair of events A_iB_k such that A_i is not the event of the space A which is most probable for a given event B_k of the space B. Clearly, it is possible to write

$$P=p(i\neq i_k).$$

Lemma 2.2.

If for a given ε $(0<\varepsilon<1)$, a set $\varDelta_i$ of events B_k can be associated with each A_i $(1\leqq i\leqq n)$ such that

1) $p(\varDelta_i\varDelta_j)=0$ $(i\neq j)$

2) $p_{A_i}(\varDelta_i)>1-\varepsilon$ $(1\leqq i\leqq n)$

then $P\leqq\varepsilon$.

Proof.

Obviously, we have

(2.2) $P=1-\sum_{k=1}^{m} p(A_{i_k}B_k);$ $1-P=\sum_{k=1}^{m} p(A_{i_k}B_k).$

Let us denote by $\varDelta_0$ the set of events B_k (if such exist) which are not in any of the sets B_k $(1\leqq i\leqq n)$; then, clearly, the range of summation in the last sum can be expanded into the parts $\varDelta_0, \varDelta_1, \cdots, \varDelta_n$, and therefore

$$1-P=\sum_{i=1}^{n}\sum_{B_k\in\varDelta_i} p(A_{i_k}B_k)+\sum_{B_k\in\varDelta_0} p(A_{i_k}B_k)\leqq\sum_{i=1}^{n}\sum_{B_k\in\varDelta_i} p(A_{i_k}B_k).$$

According to the definition of the subscript i_k, the right side of this inequality can only be decreased if we replace the subscript i_k in each term of the sum by any other subscript from 1 to n. Thus, in particular

$$1-P\geqq\sum_{i=1}^{n}\sum_{B_k\in\varDelta_i} p(A_iB_k)=\sum_{i=1}^{n} p(A_i\varDelta_i)=\sum_{i=1}^{n} p(A_i)p_{A_i}(\varDelta_i)$$

$$>(1-\varepsilon)\sum_{i=1}^{n} p(A_i)=1-\varepsilon,\qquad \text{Q. E. D.}$$

As before, let n denote the number of elementary event A_i of the space A.

Lemma 2.3.

For $n > 1$

$$H_B(A) \leq P \lg (n-1) - P \lg P - (1-P) \lg (1-P).$$

Proof.

As above, for brevity, we write $f(x)$ for $x \lg x$. We have

$$H_B(A) = -\sum_k p(B_k) \sum_i f[p_{B_k}(A_i)] = H_1 + H_2$$

where

$$H_1 = -\sum_k p(B_k) f[p_{B_k}(A_{i_k})],$$

$$H_2 = -\sum_k p(B_k) \sum_{i \neq i_k} f[p_{B_k}(A_i)].$$

Putting $\lambda_k = p(B_k)$, $x_k = p_{B_k}(A_{i_k})$ in the inequality (1.5), we find by (2.2) that

$$(2.3) \quad H_1 = -\sum_k \lambda_k f(x_k) \leq -f\left(\sum_k \lambda_k x_k\right) = -f\left(\sum_k p(B_k) p_{B_k}(A_{i_k})\right)$$

$$= -f\left(\sum_k p(B_k A_{i_k})\right) = -f(1-P) = -(1-P) \lg (1-P).$$

A similar application of the inequality (1.5) yields because of (2.2)

$$(2.4) \quad -\sum_k p(B_k) f[1 - p_{B_k}(A_{i_k})] \leq -f\left(\sum_k p(B_k)[1 - p_{B_k}(A_{i_k})]\right)$$

$$= -f\left(1 - \sum_k p(B_k A_{i_k})\right) = -f(P) = -P \lg P.$$

Furthermore, since

$$1 - p_{B_k}(A_{i_k}) = \sum_{i \neq i_k} p_{B_k}(A_i),$$

then for any fixed k $(1 \leq k \leq m)$

$$f[1-p_{B_k}(A_{i_k})] = \sum_{i \neq i_k} p_{B_k}(A_i) \lg \sum_{i \neq i_k} p_{B_k}(A_i)$$

$$= (n-1)f\left(\frac{\sum\limits_{i \neq i_k} p_{B_k}(A_i)}{n-1} \right) + \lg (n-1) \sum_{i \neq i_k} p_{B_k}(A_i).$$

We again use (1.5) to estimate the first term on the right side by putting this time $\lambda_i = \dfrac{1}{n-1}$, $x_i = p_{B_k}(A_i)$ $(1 \leq i \leq n, i \neq i_k)$. This gives

$$f\left(\frac{\sum\limits_{i \neq i_k} p_{B_k}(A_i)}{n-1} \right) \leq \sum_{i \neq i_k} \frac{1}{n-1} f[p_{B_k}(A_i)],$$

and, therefore

$$f[1-p_{B_k}(A_{i_k})] \leq \sum_{i \neq i_k} f[p_{B_k}(A_i)] + \lg (n-1) \sum_{i \neq i_k} p_{B_k}(A_i).$$

Multiplying all the terms of this inequality by $p(B_k)$ and summing over k from i to m, we find by (2.2) that

$$(2.5) \qquad \sum_k p(B_k) f[1-p_{B_k}(A_{i_k})] \leq \sum_k p(B_k) \sum_{i \neq i_k} f[p_{B_k}(A_i)]$$

$$+P \lg (n-1) = -H_2 + P \lg (n-1).$$

Finally, combining (2.3), (2.4), and (2.5) term by term, we find

$$H_1 \leq -(1-P) \lg (1-P) - P \lg P - H_2 + P \lg (n-1),$$

from which

$$H_B(A) = H_1 + H_2 \leq P \lg (n-1) - P \lg P - (1-P) \lg (1-P),$$

$$\text{Q. E. D.}$$

CHAPTER II.

Ergodic Sources

#3. Concept of source. Stationarity. Entropy

In statistical communication theory, the output of every information source is regarded as a random process. The statistical structure of this process constitutes the mathematical definition of the given source. In this paper, we shall deal exclusively with *discrete* sources (processes with discrete time); the output of such a source is a sequence of random quantities (or events). Consequently, we must understand the definition of a source to be the complete probabilistic characterization of such a sequence.

Underlying the definition of every source is the set A of symbols used by it, which we call its *alphabet*, and which we always assume to be *finite*. The separate symbols of this alphabet, are called its *letters*. Let us consider a sequence of letters, infinite on both sides.

$$(3.1) \qquad x = (\cdots, x_{-1}, x_0, x_1, x_2, \cdots),$$

which represents a possible "life history" of the given source. We shall regard it as an elementary event in a certain (infinite) probability space, a space the specification of which characterizes the sequence (3.1) as a random process. The set of all sequences (3.1) (i. e., the set of all elementary events of the given space) will be denoted by A^I. Any subset of the set A^I represents an event of our space, and conversely. Thus, for example, the event "the source emits the letter α at time t

and the letter β at time u " is the set of all sequences x of the form (3.1) for which

$$x_t = \alpha, \qquad x_u = \beta.$$

Generally, if $t_1, t_2, \cdots, t_n$ are any integers and $\alpha_1, \alpha_2, \cdots, \alpha_n$ are any letters of the alphabet A, then the event "the source emits the letter α_i at time t_i $(1 \leq i \leq n)$" is the set of all x for which

$$x_{t_i} = \alpha_i \qquad (1 \leq i \leq n).$$

Subsequently, we shall call such a set of elementary events x a *cylinder set*, or briefly a *cylinder*. As is well known, it is sufficient to know the probability $\mu(Z)$ of all cylinders Z to define the sequence (3.1) as a random process. Let us consider the set of all cylinders of the given alphabet A and its *Borel extension* F_A, i.e., the intersection of all the Borel fields which contain all the cylinders of the alphabet A. Then, giving the probabilities $\mu(Z)$ of all cylinders Z uniquely determines the probability $\mu(S)$ of any set $S \in F_A$ of elementary events x. Thus a complete description of the source as a random process is achieved by specifying 1) an alphabet A, and 2) a probability measure $\mu(S)$ defined for all $S \in F_A$. In particular, we always have $\mu(A^I) = 1$. Since the alphabet A and the probability measure μ completely characterize the statistical nature of the source, we can denote the source by the symbol $[A, \mu]$.

In his basic work [1], Shannon considered only sources with the character of stationary Markov chains; the characterization of such sources is achieved by more elementary means. The general concept of source just given is due to McMillan [3].

Consider any given sequence x of the type (3.1) of letters from the alphabet A, and denote by Tx the sequence

$$Tx = (\cdots, x'_{-1}, x'_0, x'_1, x'_2, \cdots),$$

where $x'_k = x'_{k+1}$ $(-\infty < k < +\infty)$ (so that the operator T denotes the "shift" by one time unit). If S is any set of elements x, then the set TS is the set of all Tx for which $x \in S$. (In other words, the relations $x \in S$ and $Tx \in TS$ are equivalent.) It is easy to see that if $S \in F_A$ we have $TS \in F_A$; it is also obvious that the operator T maps the set A^I into itself

$$TA^I = A^I.$$

If

$$\mu(TS) = \mu(S)$$

for any set $S \in F_A$, then the source is called *stationary*. Evidently, by the stationarity of a source is meant the time invariance of the probability regime of its output. All the sources considered below will be assumed to be stationary.

From the information theory viewpoint, the most important characteristic of every source is the rate at which it emits information, i.e., the average amount of information given by one emitted symbol. We now show how to arrive at an exact definition of this quantity. Consider a sequence of n successive symbols emitted by a given source; let this sequence be x_t, $x_{t+1}, \cdots, x_{t+n-1}$. If the source alphabet A contains a letters, then the number of such different n-term sequence is obviously a^n. Every such sequence C is a cylinder in the space A^I (i.e., the set of all $x \in A^I$ for which the $x_t, \cdots, x_{t+n-1}$ assume the fixed values characterizing the given sequence), and therefore has a definite probability $\mu(C)$. Thus, the set of all possible n-term sequences of the type described represents a finite probability space consisting of a^n elementary events C with probabilities

$\mu(C)$. In chapter I we agreed to measure the amount of information contained in such a space by its entropy

$$H_n = -\sum_C \mu(C) \lg \mu(C).$$

If the given source is stationary (as we shall always assume), then the probabilities $\mu(C)$, and therefore the entropy H_n of an n-term sequence do not depend on the "initial moment" t, and are uniquely determined by the nature of the source and by the number n. Thus we can say that the sequence of n symbols emitted by the source gives a well defined amount of information H_n, which depends only on n and on the nature of the source, so that, on the average, the amount of information per symbol emitted by the source is H_n/n. Consequently, it is natural to agree to call the quantity

$$H = \lim_{n \to \infty} \frac{H_n}{n}$$

the *source entropy*, i. e., the average amount of information conveyed by one emitted symbol (if, of course, the limit exists). Clearly, the entropy H as thus defined, depends only on the nature of the source (i. e., on the alphabet A and on the probability distribution μ). The fact that the entropy really exists for every stationary source is the first fundamental theorem of the general theory of discrete sources. We turn to its proof.*

The space A_{n+m} of sequences of length $n+m$ (where n and m are positive integers) can be regarded as the product of the space A_n of sequences of length n and the space A_m of sequences of length m (see #1). Hence, according to #1

---

* As far as I know, the first proof was given by McMillan [3]. However, McMillan had in mind a broader aim, so that his proof is considerably more formidable than the one given below.

$$H(A_{n+m}) = H(A_n) + H_{A_n}(A_m); \qquad H_{A_n}(A_m) \leqq H(A_m),$$

from which

$$H(A_n) \leqq H(A_{n+m}) \leqq H(A_n) + H(A_m).$$

In our new notation, this can be written as

$$H_n \leqq H_{n+m} \leqq H_n + H_m.$$

In particular, the first of these inequalities yields (for $m=1$)

(3.2) $$H_n \leqq H_{n+1},$$

and the second is easily extended to any number of terms and, in particular, gives for any integral k

(3.3) $$H_{kn} \leqq kH_n.$$

Setting $n=1$ in (3.3), we find that for any $k \geqq 1$.

$$H_k \leqq kH_1,$$

which shows that

$$a = \liminf_{n \to \infty} \frac{H_n}{n} < +\infty.$$

Now let $\varepsilon > 0$ be given arbitrarily, and let the subscript q be chosen such that

$$\frac{H_q}{q} < a + \varepsilon.$$

For any $n > q$, we determine an integer $k > 1$ such that

$$(k-1)q < n \leqq kq.$$

Then, because of (3.2)

$$H_n \leqq H_{kq}.$$

Consequently, by (3.3)

$$\frac{H_n}{n} \leq \frac{H_{kq}}{(k-1)q} \leq \frac{k}{k-1}\frac{H_q}{q} < \frac{k}{k-1}(a+\varepsilon),$$

and therefore, for sufficiently large n (and hence for appropriately large k)

$$a-\varepsilon < \frac{H_n}{n} < \frac{k}{k-1}(a+\varepsilon) < a+2\varepsilon.$$

But since ε is arbitrarily small

$$\lim_{n\to\infty}\frac{H_n}{n} = a, \qquad \text{Q. E. D.}$$

♯4. Ergodic Sources

The set S of elements $x \in A^I$ is called *invariant* if $TS=S$, i.e., if the "shift operator" T carries the set into itself. The set A^I is always invariant. For any $x \in A^I$, the set of elements $\cdots, T^{-1}x, x, Tx, T^2x, \cdots$ is always an invariant set. The source $[A, \mu]$ is called *ergodic* if the probability $\mu(S)$ of every invariant set $S \in F_A$ is either 0 or 1. The ergodic property is very important in the study of the statistical structure of the source. This results from the following considerations. Each (numerically valued) function $f(x)$ of the elementary event $x \in A^I$ can be regarded as a random variable defined on the space A^I, and conversely. If the abstract Lebesgue integral

(4.1) $$\int_{A^I} |f(x)| d\mu(x) < +\infty,$$

then this random variable has the mathematical expectation

$$Mf(x) = \int_{A^I} f(x)\, d\mu(x).$$

The well-known "ergodic theorem" of Birkhoff states that

for any stationary source $[A, \mu]$ and for every summable function $f(x)$ (i.e., satisfying the requirement (4.1)) the limit

$$\lim_{n \to \infty} \frac{1}{n} \sum_{k=0}^{n-1} f(T^k x) = h(x)$$

exists almost everywhere (i.e., with probability 1) where the function $h(x)$ is invariant, i.e., $h(Tx) = h(x)$ for all x for which $h(x)$ exists. If the source $[A, \mu]$ is ergodic, then almost everywhere (with probability 1)

$$h(x) = M f(x);$$

thus, in the case of an ergodic source, the ratio

$$\frac{\sum_{k=0}^{n-1} f(T^k x)}{n}$$

approaches the mathematical expectation of $f(x)$ as $n \to \infty$, for almost all x.

Now let $g_S(x)$ be the characteristic function of the set $S \in F_A$ (i.e., $g_S(x) = 1$ $(x \in S)$ and $g_S(x) = 0$ $(x \notin S)$). Obviously, $g_S(x)$ is summable and $M g_S(x) = \mu(S)$. The sum $\sum_{k=0}^{n-1} g_S(T^k x)$ is the number of terms of the series $x, Tx, \cdots, T^{n-1}x$ which belong to the set S. Let us denote this number by $\varphi_{n, S}(x)$. Then the Birkhoff theorem states that in the case of an ergodic source, we have for almost all x

$$\lim_{n \to \infty} \frac{\varphi_{n, S}(x)}{n} = \mu(S).$$

Thus, in this case, the proportion of the terms in the sequence

$$x, Tx, T^2 x, \cdots$$

which are elements of the set is just the probability of the set S, for almost all such sequences.

Let us agree to say that the source $[A, \mu]$ *reflects* the set $S \in F_A$, if almost everywhere (with probability 1)

$$\lim_{n \to \infty} \frac{1}{n} \sum_{k=0}^{n-1} g_S(T^k x) = \mu(S).$$

We have just seen that an ergodic source reflects any set $S \in F_A$. It is easy to convince oneself that the converse holds: If the stationary source $[A, \mu]$ reflects any set $S \in F_A$, then the source is ergodic. Indeed, if the $[A, \mu]$ source were not ergodic, then there would exist an invariant set $S \in F_A$ for which $0 < \mu(S) < 1$. Because of the invariance of S, we would have $Tx \in S$, $T^2 x \in S$, $\cdots$ for any $x \in S$ and, therefore $g_S(T^k x) = 1$ $(k = 0,1,2,\cdots)$. Consequently

$$\lim_{n \to \infty} \frac{1}{n} \sum_{k=0}^{n-1} g_S(T^k x) = 1 \neq \mu(S)$$

for any $x \in S$. Since $\mu(S) > 0$, then the set S is not reflected by the source $[A, \mu]$, Q. E. D.

A somewhat stronger theorem will be needed below: *In order for a given stationary source to be ergodic, it is sufficient for it to reflect all cylinders of the space A^I.* To see this, it is enough to show that the sets $S \in F_A$, which are reflected by a given source, generate a Borel field, for, if this field contains all cylinders of the space A^I, it contains the whole field F_A, by the very definition of the latter. But this means that the given source reflects any set $S \in F_A$ and, as we have just seen, this is sufficient for the source to be ergodic.

Let us denote by G the class of all sets $S \in F_A$ which are reflected by the given source; in our special case, G contains all cylinders of the space A^I. If the sets $S_1, S_2, \cdots, S_k$ are non-overlapping, then obviously

$$g_{S_1+\cdots+S_k}(x)=g_{S_1}(x)+\cdots+g_{S_k}(x),$$

whence it follows at once that $S_1 \in G, \cdots, S_k \in G$ implies $S_1+\cdots +S_k \in G$. Furthermore, if $S_2 \subset S_1$, then

$$g_{S_1-S_2}(x)=g_{S_1}(x)-g_{S_2}(x),$$

whence it is easy to see that $S_1-S_2 \in G$ follows from $S_1 \in G$ and $S_2 \in G$. In order to convince ourselves that G is a Borel field, it remains only to show that the rule which we established above for a finite sum of sets $S_1+\cdots+S_k$ remains valid for an infinite sum $\sum_{k=1}^{\infty} S_k$ of non-overlapping sets. For this purpose we need the following auxiliary proposition.

Lemma 4.1.

For any $\varepsilon>0$, no matter how small, there exists a $\delta>0$ such that if the set $U \in F_A$ has probability less than δ, then $\mu(S_\varepsilon)<\varepsilon$, where S_ε is the set of values of x for which $h_U(x)>\varepsilon$.

Proof.

For $x \in S_\varepsilon$

$$\lim_{n\to\infty}\frac{1}{n}\sum_{k=0}^{n-1}g_U(T^k x)=h_U(x)>\varepsilon.$$

Hence, if n is sufficiently large, we have

(4.2) $$\sum_{k=0}^{n-1}g_U(T^k x)>\frac{\varepsilon}{2}n$$

for all points x of a set S_ε' with probability

$$\mu(S_\varepsilon') \geqq \frac{1}{2}\mu(S_\varepsilon).$$

From (4.2) we find by integrating over x

(4.3) $$\sum_{k=0}^{n-1}\int_{S_\varepsilon'} g_U(T^k x)\,d\mu(x) \geqq \frac{\varepsilon n}{2}\mu(S_\varepsilon') \geqq \frac{\varepsilon n}{4}\mu(S_\varepsilon).$$

But, on the other hand, because of the stationarity of the given source

$$\int_{S'_\varepsilon} g_U(T^k x)\, d\mu(x) = \int_{S'_\varepsilon} g_U(T^k x)\, d\mu(T^k x) \leqq \mu(U) \quad (0 \leqq k < n),$$

and (4.3) gives

$$\frac{\varepsilon n}{4}\,\mu(S_\varepsilon) \leqq n\mu(U).$$

If we put $\delta = \dfrac{\varepsilon^2}{4}$, then the inequality

$$\mu(S_\varepsilon) < \varepsilon$$

follows from $\mu(U) < \delta$, which proves the lemma.

Now, let $S_i \in G$ $(i=1,2,\cdots)$, $\sum\limits_{i=1}^{\infty} S_i = S$ and let the sets S_i be non-overlapping so that the series

$$\sum_{i=1}^{\infty} \mu(S_i) = \mu(S)$$

converges. We put $\sum\limits_{i>N} S_i = U_N$, so that

$$\mu(U_N) \to 0 \quad (N \to \infty).$$

Since $S = S_1 + \cdots + S_N + U_N$, then

$$g_S(x) = g_{S_1}(x) + \cdots + g_{S_N}(x) + g_{U_N}(x).$$

and therefore

$$h_S(x) = h_{S_1}(x) + \cdots + h_{S_N}(x) + h_{U_N}(x).$$

But we have $h_{S_i}(x) = \mu(S_i)$ $(1 \leqq i \leqq N)$ with probability 1. Therefore, with probability 1, we have

$$h_S(x) = \mu\left(\sum_{i=1}^{N} S_i\right) + h_{U_N}(x).$$

But by lemma 4.1, for sufficiently large N and with probability arbitrarily close to unity, we have

$$h_{U_N}(x) < \varepsilon,$$

where $\varepsilon > 0$ is arbitrarily small. Since $h_S(x)$ is independent of N and ε, then with probability 1

$$h_S(x) = \mu(S),$$

and therefore $S \in G$. Thus, G is a Borel field, a fact which, as we have seen, completes the proof that every source which reflects all the cylinders of the space A^I is ergodic.

#5. The E property. McMillan's theorem.

If the alphabet A of a given source contains a letters, then the number of different "n-term sequences"

$$x_t, x_{t+1}, \cdots, x_{t+n-1}$$

which can be emitted by the source is a^n. As already stated in #3, these sequences C can be regarded as the elementary events of a finite probability space. The probabilities $\mu(C)$ of these elementary events are determined by specifying the source itself, since every sequence C is a cylinder of the space A^I and has the definite probability $\mu(C)$ (which in the case of a stationary source is independent of t). Thus, the different sequences C can also be regarded as compound events (cylinders) of the infinite space A^I. As long as n remains constant, the first point of view is preferable, since it is considerably simpler than the second. But if n varies in our considerations, then the first point of view becomes inconvenient, since it forces us to consider a separate space for every value of n; in such cases it is usually more advantageous to use the second point of view, since it allows us to consider all the events as occurring in one and the same space A^I.

As we have already noted in #3, every (numerical valued) function of the letters $x_t, x_{t+1}, \cdots, x_{t+n-1}$ can be regarded as a random variable on the space A^I of the given source, since the letters $x_t, x_{t+1}, \cdots, x_{t+n-1}$ as well as the value of the given function are uniquely determined by specifying the elementary event of the space A^I $(x=\cdots, x_{-1}, x_0, x_1, \cdots)$. In particular, $-(1/n)$ lg $\mu(C)$ is such a random variable, where C is a random sequence $x_t, x_{t+1}, \cdots, x_{t+n-1}$ with given n and t. (Of course, lg $\mu(C)$ is independent of t if the given source is stationary.) Clearly, this random variable assumes the same value for all x having the identical sequence $C=x_t, x_{t+1}, \cdots, x_{t+n-1}$ (i.e., belonging to the cylinder corresponding to this sequence). Consequently, the mathematical expectation of this quantity can easily be found by elementary means, i.e., by multiplying its value on each cylinder C by the probability $\mu(C)$ of the cylinder and adding all the products. This gives

$$M\left(-\frac{1}{n}\lg \mu(C)\right)=-\frac{1}{n}\sum_{C}\mu(C)\lg \mu(C).$$

Here, we recognize the sum $-\sum_{C}'\mu(C)\lg \mu(C)$ (see #3) as the entropy of n-term sequences from the given source, which we denoted by H_n. Thus we find

$$M\left[-\frac{1}{n}\lg \mu(C)\right]=\frac{H_n}{n}.$$

Assuming the given source to be stationary, we set $t=0$, so that hereafter C denotes the sequence $x_0, x_1, \cdots, x_{n-1}$. The random variable $-(1/n)\lg \mu(C)$ is then a function of x and n, which we denote by $f_n(x)$; thus

$$Mf_n(x) = \frac{H_n}{n}.$$

In #3 we showed that for any stationary source the ratio H_n/n approached a definite limit as $n \to \infty$, which we agreed to call the entropy (per letter) of the given source. Thus we find for any stationary source

$$Mf_n(x) \to H \qquad (n \to \infty),$$

i. e., *the mathematical expectation of the random variable $f_n(x)$* $= -(1/n) \lg \mu(C)$ *approaches the entropy of the given source as* $n \to \infty$.

The fact of primary significance for all of information theory is that a considerably stronger statement holds under certain simplifying assumptions about the nature of the source: Not only does the mathematical expectation of $f_n(x)$ approach H as a limit as $n \to \infty$, but $f_n(x)$ *itself converges in probability to H* as $n \to \infty$. This means that, *for arbitrarily small $\varepsilon > 0$ and δ* > 0, *the probability of the inequality* $|f_n(x) - H| > \varepsilon$ *is less than* δ *for sufficiently large n*. This can be said still more descriptively as follows, by recalling the definition of $f_n(x)$. For arbitrarily small $\varepsilon > 0$ and $\delta > 0$, and for sufficiently large n, all the n-term sequences C in the output of the given source can be separated into two groups, such that

    1) For every sequence C of the first group

$$\left| \frac{\lg \mu(C)}{n} + H \right| < \varepsilon.$$

    2) The sum of the probabilities of all the sequences of the second group is less than δ.

Let us agree to call the first group the " high probability group ", and the second group the " low probability group ".

The high probability group is characterized by the fact that $(1/n)\lg \mu(C)$ is close to $-H$ for all its sequences C, so that the probability $\mu(C)$ of such a sequence is approximately 2^{-nH}. Hence, all the sequences of the high probability group have approximately the same probability 2^{-nH}, which means that the number of sequences in this group is approximately 2^{nH}. If we recall that the number of all n-term sequences is $a^n = 2^{n \lg a}$ and that H is always $\leq \lg a$, them we see that, generally speaking (more exactly, with the exception of the case $H = \lg a$), for large n the high probability group contains only a negligibly small share of all the n-term sequences from the source. On the contrary, the overwhelming majority of such sequences fall into the low probability group.

We shall call the source property just described the E property. As already mentioned, it is of fundamental significance in information theory. Therefore it is important to find the broadest possible class of sources possessing this property. For sources such that each letter is statistically independent of all the preceding letters, the E property is an almost immediate consequence of the law of large numbers, and always holds; however, in practice, we seldom encounter such sources. As Shannon showed (see [1], also [5], Theorem 3), all sources of the simple ergodic Markov chain type also possess the E property, and this proof is easily carried over to the case of compound Markov chains of any order. Finally, in 1953, McMillan succeeded in proving that any ergodic source possesses the E property. This important theorem permitted for the first time the construction of a mathematical basis for the general theory of information with sufficiently broad assumptions on the statistical nature of the transmitted information. We shall give a detailed proof of McMillan's theorem in subsequent sections. In doing so, we shall refer to certain "ergodic theorems" of a general character, which, like Birkhoff's theorem (already cited more than once), we must assume to be known to the reader.

#6. The martingale concept. Doob's theorem.

In recent years, the concept of *martingale*, introduced by Doob, has been useful in various problems of probability theory. Here, we must become acquainted with this concept in a rather limited form corresponding to our needs.

Let

$$(6.1) \qquad \xi_1, \xi_2, \cdots, \xi_m, \cdots$$

be a sequence of random variables defined on the space of elementary events $x \in A^I$. (The sequence of functions $f_n(x)$ which we considered in the previous section is such a sequence.) In general, the ξ_m are mutually dependent, and, for $m > 1$, we can speak of the conditional mathematical expectation of ξ_m for given values of $\xi_1, \cdots, \xi_{m-1}$. Let us agree to denote the conditional mathematical expectation of ξ_m for $\xi_1 = a_1, \xi_2 = a_2, \cdots, \xi_{m-1} = a_{m-1}$ by $M_{a_1 a_2 \cdots a_{m-1}}(\xi_m)$.

The sequence (6.1) is called a *martingale* if for any $m > 1$ and any a_i

$$(6.2) \qquad M_{a_1 \cdots a_{m-1}}(\xi_m) = a_{m-1}.$$

We call the martingale (6.1) bounded if the random variables ξ_m are all bounded ($|\xi_m| < C$ for any x and m). In what follows, we deal only with bounded martingales, so that the question of the existence of the mathematical expectations which we need causes no difficulty.

By the "sequence $a_m, \cdots, a_n$", where $m \leq n$, we mean the set (cylinder) of those $x \in A$ for which $\xi_i = a_i$ $(m \leq i \leq n)$. Let A_{m-1} be the sequence $a_1, \cdots, a_{m-1}$; then

$$M_{a_1 \cdots a_{m-1}}(\xi_m) = \frac{1}{\mu(A_{m-1})} \int_{A_{m-1}} \xi_m(x)\, d\mu(x),$$

and the characteristic requirement (6.2), defining the martingale, can be written as

$$\int_{A_{m-1}} \xi_m(x)\, d\mu(x) = a_{m-1}\mu(A_{m-1}).$$

The fundamental theorem of Doob [7], which we need, is that *every bounded martingale converges with probability 1* (almost everywhere in A^I). We need two auxiliary propositions in order to prove it.

Lemma 6.1.

Let $\xi_1, \xi_2, \cdots, \xi_m, \cdots$ be a bounded martingale, and let A_j be one of the sequences $a_1, a_2, \cdots, a_j$, where $m > j$. Then

(6.3) $$\int_{A_j} \xi_m\, d\mu(x) = \int_{A_j} \xi_j\, d\mu(x) = a_j \mu(A_j).$$

(*In other words, the conditional mathematical expectation of ξ_m is a_j, for given $a_1, \cdots, a_j$*).

Proof.

For $m = j+1$, (6.3) follows from the definition of a martingale. Consequently, let $m > j+1$. Then

$$\int_{A_j} \xi_m\, d\mu(x) = \sum_s \int_{A_j C_s} \xi_m\, d\mu(x)$$

where the summation is over all sequences C_s of the form $a_{j+1}, \cdots, a_{m-1}$. For any sequence C_s, the intersection $A_j C_s$ is some sequence $a_1, \cdots, a_{m-1}$, so that, by the martingale definition

$$\int\limits_{A_j C_s} \xi_m \, d\mu(x) = a_{m-1} \mu(A_j C_s) = \int\limits_{A_j C_s} \xi_{m-1} \, d\mu(x).$$

(since $\xi_{m-1} = a_{m-1}$ for any $x \in A_j C_s$). Summing this equality over all the sequences C_s, we find (for $m > j+1$)

$$\int\limits_{A_j} \xi_m \, d\mu(x) = \int\limits_{A_j} \xi_{m-1} \, d\mu(x).$$

Clearly, the successive application of this recurrence relation leads to (6.3) and Lemma 6.1 is proved.

Lemma 6.2.

Let $n > m > 0$, let N be a set of sequences $a_1, \cdots, a_m$, and let Λ be the set of all sequences $a_m, \cdots, a_n$ for which

$$\min_{m \leq j \leq n} a_j \leq k,$$

where k is any given real number. Then, for $r > n$

$$\int\limits_{\Lambda N} \xi_r(x) \, d\mu(x) \leq k \, \mu(\Lambda N).$$

Proof.

We denote by Λ_j $(m \leq j \leq n)$ the set of all sequences $a_m,$ $\cdots, a_n$ for which

$$a_m > k, \cdots, a_{j-1} > k, a_j \leq k.$$

Clearly, the sets Λ_j $(m \leq j \leq n)$ are non-overlapping and have the set Λ as their union. It is also clear that each Λ_j is a certain set of sequences $a_1, \cdots, a_j$ (i. e., whether $x \in \Lambda_j$ or not is completely determined by the values of the quantities $\xi_1(x)$ $= a_1, \cdots, \xi_j(x) = a_j$). We have

$$(6.4) \qquad \int_{\Lambda N} \xi_r \, d\mu(x) = \sum_{j=m}^{n} \int_{\Lambda_j N} \xi_r \, d\mu(x).$$

But each $\Lambda_j N$ is, evidently, a certain set of sequences $C_s^{(j)}$ of the type $a_1, \cdots, a_j$, $\Lambda_j N = \sum_s C_s^{(j)}$, so that by Lemma 6.1 for $r > n$

$$\int_{\Lambda_j N} \xi_r \, d\mu(x) = \sum_s \int_{C_s^{(j)}} \xi_r \, d\mu(x) = \sum_s \int_{C_s^{(j)}} \xi_j \, d\mu(x) = \int_{\Lambda_j N} \xi_j \, d\mu(x).$$

Since $\xi_j = a_j \leq k$ on the set Λ_j, then

$$\int_{\Lambda_j N} \xi_r \, d\mu(x) \leq k \, \mu(\Lambda_j N) \qquad (m \leq j \leq n),$$

and, therefore, by (6.4)

$$\int_{\Lambda N}^{\bullet} \xi_r \, d\mu(x) \leq k \, \mu(\Lambda N), \qquad \text{Q. E. D.}$$

Remark.

It is clear that

$$\int_{\Lambda N} \xi_r \, d\mu(x) \geq k \, \mu(\Lambda N)$$

can be proved in a completely analogous way if Λ is the set of all sequences $a_m, \cdots, a_n$ for which

$$\max_{m \leq j \leq n} a_j \geq k.$$

Doob's Theorem.

Every bounded martingale (6.1) *converges with probability 1 (i.e., almost everywhere in A^I).*

Proof.

Suppose the theorem is incorrect. Then, real numbers k_1 and k_2 can be found such that

$$\liminf_{n \to \infty} \xi_n < k_1 < k_2 < \limsup_{n \to \infty} \xi_n$$

on a set Λ of positive probability. We put $\mu(\Lambda)=\eta>0$. Clearly, we can select a positive integer n_1 so large that

$$\max_{1\leq j\leq n_1} \xi_j \geq k_2$$

on a set Λ_1 for which

$$\mu(\Lambda\Lambda_1) > \eta\left(1-\frac{1}{3}\right).$$

Furthermore, if n_2 is large enough, we have

$$\min_{n_1\leq j\leq n_2} \xi_j \leq k_1$$

on a set Λ_2 for which

$$\mu(\Lambda\Lambda_2) > \eta\left(1-\frac{1}{3^2}\right);$$

again, if n_3 is large enough

$$\max_{n_2\leq j\leq n_3} \xi_j \geq k_2$$

on a set Λ_3 for which

$$\mu(\Lambda\Lambda_3) > \eta\left(1-\frac{1}{3^3}\right),$$

etc. We continue this alternating process indefinitely. We put

$$\Lambda_1\Lambda_2\cdots\Lambda_k = M_k \quad (k=1,2,\cdots).$$

For any $k\geq 1$, we have

$$\mu(M_k) \geq \mu(\Lambda M_k) = \mu(\Lambda) - \mu(\Lambda\overline{M}_k) = \eta - \mu\left\{\sum_{i=1}^{k}(\Lambda-\Lambda\Lambda_i)\right\}$$

$$\geq \eta - \sum_{i=1}^{k}\mu(\Lambda-\Lambda\Lambda_i) = \eta - \sum_{i=1}^{k}[\mu(\Lambda)-\mu(\Lambda\Lambda_i)]$$

$$\geq \eta - \sum_{i=1}^{k}\left[\eta-\eta\left(1-\frac{1}{3^i}\right)\right] = \eta - \eta\sum_{i=1}^{k}\frac{1}{3^i} > \eta - \frac{\eta}{2} = \frac{\eta}{2}.$$

Furthermore, we have for any $r\geq 1$

$$M_{2r} = \Lambda_{2r}M_{2r-1}.$$

It is clear that in this expression M_{2r-1} is some set of sequences $a_1, a_2, \cdots, a_{n_{2r-1}}$ and $\varLambda_{2r}$ is the set of sequences $a_{n_{2r-1}}, \cdots, a_{n_{2r}}$ for which

$$\min_{n_{2r-1} \leqq j \leqq n_{2r}} a_j \leqq k_1.$$

Thus, we see that if we put $m = n_{2r-1}$, $n = n_{2r}$, $N = M_{2r-1}$, $\varLambda = \varLambda_{2r}$, $k = k_1$ in Lemma 6.2, then all the premises of this lemma are fulfilled, Therefore, if $m > n_{2r}$, Lemma 6.2 gives

$$\int_{M_{2r}} \xi_m \, d\mu(x) \leqq k_1 \mu(M_{2r}).$$

In a completely analogous way (see the remark after the proof of Lemma 6.2), we have

$$\int_{M_{2r-1}} \xi_m \, d\mu(x) \geqq k_2 \mu(M_{2r-1}).$$

Therefore, putting $M_{2r-1} - M_{2r} = Q_r$, we find

$$\int_{Q_r} \xi_m \, d\mu(x) = \int_{M_{2r-1}} \xi_m \, d\mu(x) - \int_{M_{2r}} \xi_m \, d\mu(x) \geqq k_2 \mu(M_{2r-1}) - k_1 \mu(M_{2r})$$

$$= (k_2 - k_1) \mu(M_{2r-1}) + k_1 [\mu(M_{2r-1}) - \mu(M_{2r})] >$$

$$> (k_2 - k_1) \frac{\eta}{2} + k_1 \mu(Q_r).$$

Since the sets Q_r are non-overlapping, the series $\sum_{n=1}^{\infty} \mu(Q_r)$ converges, and $\mu(Q_r) \to 0$ as $r \to \infty$. But since the left side of the last inequality does not exceed $C\mu(Q_r)$ because $|\xi_m(x)| < C$, then both the left side and the second term of the right side of this inequality are infinitesimally small as $r \to \infty$, whereas the first term of the right side is a positive constant. Thus we arrive at a contradiction which proves Doob's theorem.

#7. Auxiliary propositions

We have already remarked repeatedly (## 3,5) that every quantity which can be uniquely determined by the sequence $x_t, \cdots, x_{t+n-1}$ of letters from the alphabet A can be regarded as a function of the elementary event

$$x = \cdots, x_{-1}, x_0, x_1, \cdots$$

of the space A^I or, equivalently, as a random variable on this space. In particular, in #5 we defined such a function, viz. $f_n(x) = -(1/n) \lg \mu(C)$, where C is the sequence $x_0, x_1, \cdots, x_{n-1}$. Now we must become acquainted with some other functions of the same kind. Let us agree to denote the random sequence $x_{-n}, \cdots, x_{-1}$ by C_n, and the sequence $x_{-n}, \cdots, x_{-1}, x_0$ with one extra letter by $C_n + x_0$. Each of these sequences is an event (cylinder) of the space A^I, and every quantity which is uniquely determined by the letters $x_{-n}, \cdots, x_{-1}, x_0$ is a random variable on this space or, equivalently, a function of the elementary event x. In particular, the ratio

$$p_n(x) = \frac{\mu(C_n + x_0)}{\mu(C_n)}$$

is such a quantity, and can obviously be regarded as the conditional probability of the appearance of the letter x_0 after the appearance of the sequence $C_n = x_{-n}, \cdots, x_{-1}$. In addition, let us put $p_0(x) = \mu(x_0)$.

Let α be any fixed letter of the alphabet A, and put

$$p_n(x, \alpha) = \frac{\mu(C_n + \alpha)}{\mu(C_n)}$$

This quantity (the probability of the appearance of the letter α after the sequence C_n) differs from $p_n(x)$ in that in $p_n(x)$

the letter x_0 depends (just as do the letters $x_{-n}, \cdots, x_{-1}$) on x, whereas the letter α which replaces it in $P_n(x, \alpha)$ is fixed and independent of x.

Lemma 7.1.

The sequence $p_n(x, \alpha)$ $(n=0,1,\cdots)$ is a martingale.

Proof.

For brevity, let us put $p_n(x, \alpha) = \xi_n$. Consider any fixed sequence of $n-1$ letters $a_{-1}, \cdots, a_{-(n-1)}$ and denote by B_{n-1} the cylinder $x_{-1} = a_{-1}, \cdots, x_{-(n-1)} = a_{-(n-1)}$ of the space A^I. Furthermore, let Γ_β denote the cylinder $x_{-n} = \beta$, where β is any letter of the alphabet A. Since $\sum_\beta \Gamma_\beta = A^I$, then

$$\int_{B_{n-1}} \xi_n \, d\mu(x) = \sum_\beta \int_{B_{n-1}\Gamma_\beta} \xi_n \, d\mu(x),$$

but, for $x \in B_{n-1}\Gamma_\beta$, we have

$$\xi_n = \frac{\mu(B_{n-1}\Gamma_\beta + \alpha)}{\mu(B_{n-1}\Gamma_\beta)}.$$

Therefore

$$\int_{B_{n-1}} \xi_n \, d\mu(x) = \sum_\beta \mu(B_{n-1}\Gamma_\beta + \alpha) = \mu(B_{n-1} + \alpha).$$

But according to the definition of the random variable

$$\xi_{n-1} = \frac{\mu(C_{n-1} + \alpha)}{\mu(C_{n-1})},$$

its value $[\xi_{n-1}]_{B_{n-1}}$ at $C_{n-1} = B_{n-1}$ (i.e., when the random cylinder C_{n-1} coincides with the cylinder B_{n-1} which we chose) equals:

$$[\xi_{n-1}]_{B_{n-1}} = \frac{\mu(B_{n-1} + \alpha)}{\mu(B_{n-1})}.$$

Therefore

(7.1) $$\int_{B_{n-1}} \xi_n \, d\mu(x) = [\xi_{n-1}]_{B_{n-1}} \mu(B_{n-1}).$$

Now, let K_{n-1} be the set of all x for which $\xi_1, \cdots, \xi_{n-1}$ take any given system of values $\xi_i = \pi_i$ $(1 \leq i \leq n-1)$. Since the numbers π_i $(1 \leq i \leq n-1)$ are uniquely determined by the selection of the cylinder B_{n-1}, the set K_{n-1} is the union of several cylinders B_{n-1}, where, of course, $[\xi_i]_{B_{n-1}} = [\xi_i]_{K_{n-1}} = \pi_i$ $(1 \leq i \leq n-1)$ for all the cylinders B_{n-1} in K_{n-1}. Thus it follows from (7.1) that

$$\int_{K_{n-1}} \xi_n \, d\mu(x) = \sum_{B_{n-1} \subset K_{n-1}} \int_{B_{n-1}} \xi_n \, d\mu(x) = \sum_{B_{n-1} \subset K_{n-1}} \pi_{n-1} \mu(B_{n-1}) = \pi_{n-1} \mu(K_{n-1}).$$

But this means that the sequence $\xi_n = p_n(x, \alpha)$ $(n \geq 0)$ is a martingale, which proves Lemma 7.1.

Lemma 7.2.

The sequence $p_n(x)$ $(n = 0, 1, \cdots)$ converges almost everywhere.

Proof.

It is clear that for every fixed $x \in A^I$, the quantity $p_n(x)$ coincides with one of the $p_n(x, \alpha)$, where α runs through all the letters of the alphabet A, and where α is the same for all n (but different for the different x). Consequently, for any n, m and for any $x \in A^I$.

$$|p_n(x) - p_m(x)| \leq \sum_\alpha |p_n(x, \alpha) - p_m(x, \alpha)|.$$

But the martingale $p_n(x, \alpha)$, being obviously bounded, converges almost everywhere, by Doob's theorem (#6), no matter what the letter α is, and, therefore, the right side of the last inequality approaches zero when n and m increase without limit; clearly this proves Lemma 7.2.

The definition which we gave of the function $p_n(x)$ assumes that $\mu(C_n) > 0$; the x for which $\mu(C_n) = 0$ are obviously a set of probability 0, and we exclude them from consideration from the outset by keeping only the x for which $\mu(C_n)>0$ for any $n \geq 0$. Thus, the sequence $p_n(x)$ is defined almost everywhere in A^I. But then the sequence of functions

$$g_n(x) = -\lg p_n(x) \quad (n=0,1,\cdots)$$

will be defined almost everywhere, where the value $g_n(x) = +\infty$ [for $p_n(x) = 0$] is not excluded for these functions.

Lemma 7.3.

Let $E_{n,k}$ $(n \geq 0, k \geq 0)$ denote the set of all x for which

$$k \leq g_n(x) < k+1;$$

then

$$(7.2) \qquad \int_{E_{n,k}} g_n(x)\,d\mu(x) \leq a(k+1)2^{-k},$$

where a is the number of letters in the alphabet A.

Proof.

We define the cylinders B_n as in the proof of Lemma 7.1, and let Z_α denote the cylinder $x_0 = \alpha$, where α is any letter of the alphabet A. For $x \in B_n Z_\alpha$, we have:

$$g_n(x) = -\lg \frac{\mu(B_n+\alpha)}{\mu(B_n)} = -\lg \frac{\mu(B_n Z_\alpha)}{\mu(B_n)},$$

so that the value of $g_n(x)$ is uniquely determined by assigning the cylinder B_n and the letter α. It is clear that

$$B_n E_{n,k} = \sum_\alpha {}^* B_n Z_\alpha,$$

where the $\sum_\alpha {}^*$ denotes summation over those letters α for which $k \leq g_n(x) < k+1$ for $x \in B_n Z$. Therefore

$$(7.3) \qquad \int_{B_n E_{n,k}} g_n(x)\,d\mu(x) = \sum_\alpha {}^* \int_{B_n Z_\alpha} g_n(x)\,d\mu(x).$$

But in any of the integrals of the right side we have

$$k+1 > g_n(x) = - \lg \frac{\mu(B_n Z_a)}{\mu(B_n)} \geqq k,$$

so that

$$\mu(B_n Z_a) \leqq 2^{-k} \mu(B_n),$$

and (7.3) gives

$$\int_{B_n E_{n,k}} g_n(x) \, d\mu(x) \leqq {\sum_a}^* (k+1) \, \mu(B_n Z_a) \leqq a(k+1)2^{-k} \, \mu(B_n).$$

Finally, summation over all possible cylinders B_n gives

$$\int_{E_{n,k}} g_n(x) \, d\mu(x) \leqq a(k+1)2^{-k}$$

and Lemma 7.3 is proved. As we shall see immediately, the fact that this estimate is uniform with respect to n is important. In particular, the next proposition (uniform summability of the functions $g_n(x)$) is an immediate consequence of Lemma 7.3.

Lemma 7.4.

Given $L>0$, let $A_{n,L}$ be the set of $x \in A^I$ for which $g_n(x) > L$. Then, given any $\varepsilon > 0$, an $L_0 = L_0(\varepsilon)$ can be found such that

$$\int_{A_{n,L}} g_n(x) \, d\mu(x) < \varepsilon,$$

for $L \geqq L_0$, and for any $n \geqq 1$.

Another important consequence of Lemma 7.3 is that the absolute continuity of integrals of the functions $g_n(x)$ is also uniform with respect to n. Thus we have

Lemma 7.5.

Given any $\varepsilon > 0$, a $\delta > 0$ can be found such that if $E \in F_A$ and $\mu(E) < \delta$, then

$$\int_E g_n(x)\, d\mu(x) < \varepsilon, \qquad (n=1,2,\cdots).$$

Proof.

By Lemma 7.4, an $L = L(\varepsilon)$ can be found such that

$$\int_{A_{n,L}} g_n(x)\, d\mu(x) < \varepsilon, \qquad (n=1,2,\cdots).$$

Put $\delta = \dfrac{\varepsilon}{L}$ and let $\mu(E) < \delta$. Then

$$\int_E g_n(x)\, d\mu(x) = \int_{E A_{n,L}} g_n(x)\, d\mu(x) + \int_{\overline{E A_{n,L}}} g_n(x)\, d\mu(x)$$

$$\leq \int_{A_{n,L}} g_n(x)\, d\mu(x) + L\mu(E) < 2\varepsilon,$$

and Lemma 7.5 is proved. A consequence is that almost everywhere on A^I we have $g_n(x) < +\infty$ for any $n \geq 1$.

Now let us put

$$\lim_{n \to \infty} g_n(x) = g(x).$$

This limit exists almost everywhere, because of Lemma 7.2, if we permit the value $+\infty$ for $g(x)$.

Lemma 7.6.

The function $g(x)$ is summable over A^I. (In particular, this means that it can take the value $+\infty$ only on a set of probability 0.)

Proof.

For any $L > 0$ and any positive function $f(x)$, we put

$$f^L(x) = \min [L, f(x)].$$

Then obviously it follows from $g_n(x) \to g(x)$ that $g_n^L(x) \to g^L(x)$

$(n \to \infty)$. But since the functions $g_n^L(x)$ $(n=1,2,\cdots)$ are uniformly bounded, we find, using the known properties of the Lebesgue integral and Lemma 7.3, that

$$\int_{A^I} g^L(x)\,d\mu(x) = \lim_{n\to\infty} \int_{A^I} g_n^L(x)\,d\mu \leq \limsup_{n\to\infty} \int_{A^I} g_n(x)\,d\mu(x)$$

$$= \limsup_{n\to\infty} \sum_{k=0}^{\infty} \int_{E_{n,k}} g_n(x)\,d\mu(x) < a \sum_{k=0}^{\infty} (k+1)2^{-k}.$$

Since the right side is independent of L, Lemma 7.6 is proved.

Lemma 7.7.

$$\int_{A^I} |g_n(x)-g(x)|\,d\mu(x) \to 0 \quad (n \to \infty).$$

Proof.

Let $\varepsilon > 0$ be arbitrary. Let us denote by E_n the set of $x \in A^I$ for which $|g_n(x)-g(x)| > \varepsilon$. Then

$$\int_{A^I} |g_n(x)-g(x)|\,d\mu(x) = \int_{E_n} |g_n(x)-g(x)|\,d\mu(x) + \int_{\overline{E_n}} |g_n(x)-g(x)|\,d\mu(x)$$

$$\leq \int_{E_n} g_n(x)\,d\mu(x) + \int_{\overline{E_n}} g(x)\,d\mu(x) + \varepsilon.$$

Since $g_n(x) \to g(x)$ almost everywhere, $\mu(E_n) \to 0$ $(n \to \infty)$; consequently, the first integral on the right side is infinitesimally small as $n \to \infty$ by Lemma 7.5, and the same is true of the second integral by Lemma 7.6. This proves Lemma 7.7.

#8. Proof of McMillan's theorem

McMillan's theorem states (see #5) that as $n \to \infty$ the function $f_n(x)$ converges in probability to the number H, the entropy of the given source. Here

$$f_n(x) = -\frac{1}{n} \lg \mu(C),$$

where C is the random sequence (cylinder) $x_0, x_1, \cdots, x_{n-1}$ (which is, of course, uniquely determined by giving $x = \cdots, x_{-1}, x_0, x_1, \cdots$). In order to use the results of #7, we must first of all relate the functions $f_n(x)$ to the functions $g_n(x)$, which we studied in #7. This relation is established by the following proposition.

Lemma 8.1.

For all $x \in A^I$ and $n \geq 1$

$$f_n(x) = \frac{1}{n} \sum_{k=0}^{n-1} g_k(T^k x).$$

Proof.

Since we shall now deal with sequences $x_r, \cdots, x_{r+s}$ for various values of r and s, we must introduce a more extensive notation. We denote the probability of such a sequence by $\mu[x_r, \cdots, x_{r+s}]$ so that, for example

$$f_n(x) = -\frac{1}{n} \lg \mu[x_0, \cdots, x_{n-1}].$$

Similarly, the function $p_n(x)$, which we introduced in #7, can be written as

$$p_n(x) = \frac{\mu[x_{-n}, \cdots, x_0]}{\mu[x_{-n}, \cdots, x_{-1}]}.$$

From this it is clear that for $k \geq 0$

$$p_n(T^k x) = \frac{\mu[x_{k-n}, \cdots, x_k]}{\mu[x_{k-n}, \cdots, x_{k-1}]},$$

and, in particular

$$p_k(T^k x) = \frac{\mu[x_0, \cdots, x_k]}{\mu[x_0, \cdots, x_{k-1}]}.$$

This equality holds for $k \geq 1$. Since $p_0(x) = \mu[x_0]$ by definition, then

$$p_0(T^0 x) = p_0(x) = \mu[x_0],$$

so that

$$\prod_{k=0}^{n-1} p_k(T^k x) = \mu[x_0] \cdot \frac{\mu[x_0, x_1]}{\mu[x_0]} \cdots \frac{\mu[x_0, \cdots, x_{n-1}]}{\mu[x_0, \cdots, x_{n-2}]} = \mu[x_0, \cdots, x_{n-1}].$$

Taking the logarithm of this equality yields

$$\sum_{k=0}^{n-1} g_k(T^k x) = -\log \mu[x_0, \cdots, x_{n-1}] = n f_n(x),$$

and Lemma 8.1 is proved.

McMillan's Theorem.

For any stationary source the sequence $f_n(x)$ converges in the L^1-mean (and therefore also in probability) to some invariant function $h(x)$. In the case of an ergodic source, $h(x)$ coincides almost everywhere in A^I with the entropy H of the source.

Remark.

$f_n(x)$ is said to approach $h(x)$ in the L^1-mean if

$$\int_{A^I} |f_n(x) - h(x)| \, d\mu(x) \to 0 \quad (n \to \infty);$$

it is well-known that this implies that $f_n(x)$ converges to $h(x)$ in probability. As already noted, the function $h(x)$ is called invariant if $h(Tx) = h(x)$ $(x \in A^I)$.

Proof.

One of the familiar forms of the ergodic theorem ([8], p. 31, Satz 10; [9], equation (2.42)) states that for any function $g(x)$ which is summable over A^I, the quantity

$$\frac{1}{n} \sum_{k=0}^{n-1} g(T^k x)$$

approaches an invariant function $h(x)$ in the L^1-mean as $n \to \infty$. In particular, this holds for our function $g(x)$ because of Lemma 7.6. But by Lemma 8.1 we have

$$\int_{A^I} |f_n(x) - h(x)| \, d\mu(x) = \int_{A^I} \left| \frac{1}{n} \sum_{k=0}^{n-1} g_k(T^k x) - h(x) \right| d\mu(x)$$

$$\leq \int_{A^I} \left| \frac{1}{n} \sum_{k=0}^{n-1} [g_k(T^k x) - g(T^k x)] \right| d\mu(x) + \int_{A^I} \left| \frac{1}{n} \sum_{k=0}^{n-1} g(T^k x) - h(x) \right| d\mu(x)$$

$$\leq \frac{1}{n} \sum_{k=0}^{n-1} \int_{A^I} |g_k(x) - g(x)| \, d\mu(x) + \int_{A^I} \left| \frac{1}{n} \sum_{k=0}^{n-1} g(T^k x) - h(x) \right| d\mu(x),$$

where in transforming the first term we use the stationarity of the source. ($d\mu(x)$ is replaced by $d\mu(T^k x)$, and then $T^k x$ is introduced as a new variable of integration.)

Consider each of the two terms on the right side separately. In the first term, the summands with increasing index approach zero by Lemma 7.7. Therefore, their average value, i.e., the whole first term on the right side, approaches zero as $n \to \infty$. The same is true for the second term by the very definition of the function $h(x)$. Thus we find

$$\int_{A^I} |f_n(x) - h(x)| \, d\mu(x) \to 0 \quad (n \to \infty),$$

which proves the first part of McMillan's theorem.

In the case of an ergodic source, the ergodic theorem cited above states that the function $h(x)$ is almost everywhere a constant h. Thus, to prove the second part of McMillan's theorem, we must show that $h = H$. But from

$$\int_{A^I} |f_n(x) - h| \, d\mu(x) \to 0 \quad (n \to \infty),$$

it follows that

$$\lim_{n \to \infty} \int_{A^I} f_n(x)\, d\mu(x) = \int_{A^I} h\, d\mu(x) = h.$$

The integral on the left side is the mathematical expectation of $f_n(x)$ which, as we saw in #5, approaches H as $n \to \infty$. This means that $h = H$, which completes the proof of McMillan's theorem.

In particular, therefore, we have proved that every ergodic source has the E property: *For arbitrarily small $\varepsilon > 0$ and $\delta > 0$, and sufficiently large n, all the a^n n-term sequences of the source output are divided into two groups, a high probability group, such that $|(1/n) \lg \mu(C) + H| < \varepsilon$ for each of its sequences, and a low probability group, such that the sum of the probabilities of its sequences is less than δ.*

CHAPTER III.

Channels and the sources driving them

♯9. Concept of channel. Noise. Stationarity. Anticipation and memory

From a physical point of view, by a source is meant an apparatus which emits signals. The medium over which the signal is *transmitted*, is called a channel. The concept of channel, as well as the concept of source, plays a fundamental role in information theory. Just as in Chapter II we started the theory of sources by giving their precise mathematical characterization, we must now do the same thing for channels. We saw that the elements which can be used to characterize a source mathematically are its alphabet A, the probability space A^I with elementary events x, and the probability measure $\mu(S)$ defined on the sets $S \in F_A$. What mathematical elements can be used to characterize a given channel?

First of all, we must have a list of the signals which the channel in question can transmit. We shall always assume that this list is finite, and we shall call it the *input alphabet* (or the *alphabet at the input*) of the channel. The signals in this alphabet are called its *letters*. In general, the signals that emerge from a channel have an entirely different nature from the transmitted signals. Therefore, in addition to the input alphabet, we must know the *output alphabet* (or alphabet at the output) of the given channel, i.e., the list of signals (*letters*) which the channel can emit. We shall also always assume that the output alphabet is finite.

If every transmitted signal a (a letter of the input alphabet A) gives at the output a unique letter $b=b(a)$ of the output alphabet B, the channel is called a *noiseless channel*. In general, the presence of interference (noise) causes *different* letters $b \in B$ to be obtained at the output in different cases when the *same* letter $a \in A$ is transmitted. Since it is natural to regard the interference (noise) as a random phenomenon, and it governs which letter $b \in B$ appears at the channel output when a given signal $a \in A$ is transmitted, then we can speak of the *probability* of obtaining the letter $b \in B$ at the channel output, given that the letter $a \in A$ was transmitted. In many cases, this probability depends not only on a but also on the sequence of signals transmitted earlier, and this dependence must often be taken into account. Therefore, at the outset it is expedient to give the most general form to the phenomenon described. As in Chapter II, we shall consider the set A^I of all sequences

$$x = \cdots, x_{-1}, x_0, x_1, \cdots \quad (x_i \in A; \; -\infty < i < +\infty).$$

To every such sequence of transmitted signals corresponds a sequence

$$y = \cdots, y_{-1}, y_0, y_1, \cdots \quad (y_i \in B; \; -\infty < i < +\infty)$$

of received (output) signals. The probability that y_n will be a given letter $b \in B$ must be regarded, in the general case, as depending on the whole set of signals x_i sent, i.e., as a function of $x \in A^I$. We can denote this probability by $\nu_x(y_n=b)$. We can also say that $\nu_x(y_n=b)$ is the conditional probability (for a given sequence $x \in A^I$ of transmitted signals) that the sequence $y \in B^I$ of received signals will belong to the cylinder $y_n=b$. It is clear that in order to characterize the channel completely we must know such conditional probabilities not only for the simplest cylinders of the type $y_n = b$, but also for sets $S \subset B^I$ of more complex structure. It is natural to require that such probabilities $\nu_x(S)$ be assigned for all cylinders $S \subset B^I$; in this way, $\nu_x(S)$ will be automatically defined for all sets S in the Borel field F_B generated by the set of these cylinders.

Thus, we shall consider a channel to be specified if we know the following three elements: 1) the input alphabet A, 2) the output alphabet B, 3) the probability $\nu_x(S)$ that the y received when a given x is transmitted belongs to the set $S \in F_B$. (This probability must be given for any $x \in A^I$ and any $S \in F_B$.) We shall denote the channel specified by these elements by $[A, \nu_x, B]$. Evidently, $\nu_x(S)$ must be understood to be a one-parameter (with parameter x) family of probability measures defined on the space of elementary events B^I. We shall call the channel $[A, \nu_x, B]$ *stationary* if, for all $x \in A^I$ and $S \in F_B$

$$\nu_{Tx}(TS) = \nu_x(S),$$

where T is the same shift operator with which we were concerned in the preceding chapter.

In the majority of applications, the probability $\nu_x(y_n = b)$ that y_n coincides with a given letter $b \in B$ does not depend on all the letters $x = \cdots, x_{-1}, x_0, x_1, \cdots$ of the transmitted message, but only on those with indices rather close to n. First of all, we shall always assume that the distribution of y_n is independent of the transmitted signals that are transmitted after x_n, i.e., is independent of x_k for $k > n$; this means that $\nu_x(y_n = b)$ has the same value for all transmitted messages x for which the signals $\cdots, x_{n-1}, x_n$ are identical. In this case, we speak of a *channel without anticipation*. As regards the signals $x_{n-1}, x_{n-2}, \cdots$ preceding x_n, in the majority of cases only a limited number of them (e.g., $x_{n-1}, x_{n-2}, \cdots, x_{n-m}$) can influence the distribution of y_n. This means that the probability $\nu_x(y_n = b)$ is the same for all x with identical $x_{n-m}, \cdots, x_{n-1}, x_n$. In this case, we speak of a *channel with a finite memory*. The smallest number m for which the above holds, is called the *memory* of the channel; in particular, the distribution of y_n for a channel without memory ($m = 0$) depends only on x_n.

#10. Connection of the channel to the source

Suppose we have a channel $[A, \nu_x, B]$ and a source $[A, \mu]$ for which the alphabet A coincides with the input alphabet of the channel. Then, clearly, the channel $[A, \nu_x, B]$ can be used directly to transmit the output of the source $[A, \mu]$. Each symbol x_n emitted by the source is one of the letters of the alphabet A, and therefore can act as an input to the channel $[A, \nu_x, B]$. Then at the channel output we obtain a letter y_n of the alphabet B. When the letters from some message

$$x = \cdots, x_{-1}, x_0, x_1, \cdots$$

from the given source are fed into the channel one at a time, we obtain at the output the corresponding sequence

$$y = \cdots, y_{-1}, y_0, y_1, \cdots$$

of letters from the alphabet B. In the general case, the distribution law of every letter y_n of this sequence depends on the entire sequence x, and is determined by the probability measure ν_x. For a channel without anticipation, this distribution law depends only on the symbols $\cdots, x_{n-1}, x_n$; if, in addition, the channel has finite memory m, then the distribution of y_n depends only on $x_{n-m}, \cdots, x_n$.

This whole situation is described by saying that the source $[A, \mu]$ *feeds* (*drives*) the channel $[A, \nu_x, B]$. From the probabilistic point of view, such a connection of the channel and the source is a phenomenon in which chance intervenes in two ways: 1) the choice of the message $x \in A^I$ is random (this randomness is governed by the distribution μ, and 2) for a given $x \in A^I$, the $y \in B^I$ which is received at the channel output is random, because of the presence of noise. (This randomness is governed by the distribution ν_x.)

Consider now the probability space in which the elementary events are all possible pairs (x, y), $x \in A^I$, $y \in B^I$. Let B be the set of all pairs (a, b), where $a \in A$, $b \in B$. We can regard C as a new alphabet; then, it is natural to denote by C^I the set of pairs (x, y) of which we just spoke. Thus the specification of $(x, y) \in C^I$ is equivalent to the specification of $x \in A^I$, $y \in B^I$.

We must now introduce probabilities into the space C^I. Let $M \subset A^I$, $N \subset B^I$, i.e., let M be some set of elements x and N some set of elements y; indeed, let $M \in F_A$ (so that $\mu(M)$ has a definite value) and let $N \in F_B$. Then it is clear that the direct product $S = M \times N$ of the sets M and N is a set of pairs (x, y), so that $S \subset C^I$. The probability $\omega(S)$ of this set of the space C^I should naturally be understood to be the probability of the joint event $x \in M$, $y \in N$. But the distribution in the space of elementary events $x \in A^I$ is determined by the μ law, and, for a given x, the distribution in the space of elementary events $y \in B^I$ is determined by the ν_x law. Therefore

$$(10.1) \qquad \omega(S) = \omega(M \times N) = \int_M \nu_x(N) \, d\mu(x).$$

In particular, every cylinder $Z \subset C^I$ is obviously the direct product of a cylinder $Z_1 \subset A^I$ and a cylinder $Z_2 \subset B^I$. Therefore, Eq.

(10.1) tells us the probability of any such cylinder Z. It follows by the general property of Borel sets that the probability $\omega(S)$ is uniquely defined for any set $S \in F_C$.

Thus we see that connecting the channel $[A, \nu_x, B]$ to the source $[A, \mu]$ driving it uniquely determines a new source $[C, \omega]$. The alphabet of this source is the direct product $A \times B$; the set C^I of elementary events (x, y) is the direct product $A^I \times B^I$, and the probability measure $\omega(S)$ is given by (10.1) in the way described above. In what follows, we shall call this new source $[C, \omega]$ the *compound* source constructed by connecting the channel $[A, \nu_x, B]$ to the source $[A, \mu]$. Since we shall deal only with stationary sources and channels, the following almost obvious theorem will be of importance to us.

Theorem.

If the source $[A, \mu]$ and the channel $[A, \nu_x, B]$ are stationary, then the source $[C, \omega]$ is also stationary.

Proof.

Suppose $S \subset C^I$ and $S = X \times Y$, $X \in F_A$, $Y \in F_B$. Then, first of all, it is obvious that $TS = TX \times TY$. Therefore, Eq. (10.1) gives

$$\omega(TS) = \int_{x \in TX} \nu_x(TY) \, d\mu(x),$$

or, after substituting a new variable of integration

$$\omega(TS) = \int_{Tz \in TX} \nu_{Tz}(TY) \, d\mu(Tz).$$

Since the source $[A, \mu]$ is stationary, $d\mu(Tz) = d\mu(z)$, and since the channel $[A, \nu_x, B]$ is stationary, $\nu_{Tz}(TY) = \nu_z(Y)$; therefore

$$\omega(TS) = \int_{z \in X} \nu_z(Y) \, d\mu(z) = \omega(S).$$

We have established this equality for all $S=X\times Y$, in particular, for all cylinders $S\subset C^I$; therefore it is also valid for all $S\in F_C$. This proves the theorem.

Let us put $M=A^I$ in Eq. (10.1), while leaving $N\in F_B$ arbitrary. The quantity $\omega(M\times N)$ is then the probability of the joint event $x\in A^I$, $y\in N$, and since the first of these two events is sure, $\omega(M\times N)$ is simply the probability $\eta(N)$ of obtaining a sequence y belonging to the set $N\in F_B$ at the channel output. Thus we see that the distribution $\eta(N)$ plays the same role for the space B^I as $\mu(M)$ does for the space A^I. For $M=A^I$, equation (10.1) becomes

$$(10.2) \qquad \eta(N)=\omega(A^I\times N)=\int_{A^I} \nu_x(N)\,d\mu(x).$$

Thus we can speak of the source $[B,\eta]$ at the channel output. This source, with the sequence

$$y=\cdots, y_{-1}, y_0, y_1, \cdots$$

of letters from the alphabet B as its output, is uniquely determined (by using (10.2)) by the data of our problem, i.e., by the source A and the channel $[A,\nu_x,B]$. (Of course, the source $[C,\omega]$ considered above is uniquely determined by the same data.) If the source $[A,\mu]$ and the channel $[A,\nu_x,B]$ are stationary, then, as we proved, the source $[C,\omega]$ is also stationary; but then

$$\eta(TN)=\omega(A^I\times TN)=\omega(TA^I\times TN)=\omega(A^I\times N)=\eta(N),$$

and therefore the source $[B,\eta]$ is also stationary.

We proved in #3 that every stationary source has a definite entropy. Therefore, if the source $[A,\mu]$ and the channel $[A,\nu_x,B]$ are stationary, each of the three sources $[A,\mu]$, $[B,\eta]$

and $[C, \omega]$ has a definite entropy. Let us agree to denote these three entropies by $H(X)$, $H(Y)$, and $H(X, Y)$, respectively. We defined the entropy $H(X)$ as follows. Let $H_n(X)$ be the entropy of the finite space the elementary events of which are all the n-term sequences $x_0, \cdots, x_{n-1}$ (cylinders) emitted by the source $[A, \mu]$, with corresponding probabilities determined by the distribution μ; then

$$H(X) = \lim_{n \to \infty} \frac{1}{n} H_n(X).$$

In complete analogy

$$H(Y) = \lim_{n \to \infty} \frac{1}{n} H_n(Y),$$

$$H(X, Y) = \lim_{n \to \infty} \frac{1}{n} H_n(X, Y),$$

where correspondingly $H_n(Y)$ and $H_n(X, Y)$ denote the entropies of the finite spaces of sequences $y_0, \cdots, y_{n-1}$ from the source $[B, \eta]$ and $x_0, y_0, \cdots, x_{n-1}, y_{n-1}$ from the source $[C, \omega]$.

But giving the "pair sequence" $x_0, y_0, \cdots, x_{n-1}, y_{n-1}$ is obviously equivalent to giving the pair of sequences $x_0, \cdots, x_{n-1}$ and $y_0, \cdots, y_{n-1}$, so that the space of sequences $x_0, y_0, \cdots, x_{n-1}, y_{n-1}$ is the product of the spaces of sequences $x_0, \cdots, x_{n-1}$ and $y_0, \cdots$ y_{n-1}. Therefore, as we saw in #1

$$H_n(X, Y) = H_n(X) + H_{nX}(Y) = H_n(Y) + H_{nY}(X),$$

where $H_{nX}(Y)$ denotes the average conditional entropy of the space of sequences $y_0, \cdots, y_{n-1}$ for a given sequence $x_0, \cdots, x_{n-1}$, and $H_{nY}(X)$ has an analogous meaning. It follows that

$$H_{nX}(Y) = H_n(X, Y) - H_n(X),$$

$$H_{nY}(X) = H_n(X, Y) - H_n(Y).$$

Dividing all the terms of these equalities by n, and passing to the limit as $n \to \infty$, we find

(10.3)
$$\begin{cases} \lim_{n \to \infty} \dfrac{1}{n} H_{nX}(Y) = H(X, Y) - H(X), \\[2mm] \lim_{n \to \infty} \dfrac{1}{n} H_{nY}(X) = H(X, Y) - H(Y). \end{cases}$$

This means, first of all, that the limits on the left always exist. Let us denote them by $H_X(Y)$ and $H_Y(X)$, respectively. Consider the conditional entropy per symbol of the output of the source $[B, \eta]$ for a given output x of the source $[A, \mu]$; then $H_X(Y)$ can be interpreted as the average of this entropy over x. $H_Y(X)$ has a similar meaning with the roles of the sources $[A, \mu]$ and $[B, \eta]$ interchanged.

In practice, this latter quantity is of the greatest interest. Let us recall that, on the one hand, we regarded the entropy of any finite space as a measure of the uncertainty contained in the space, and, on the other hand, as a measure of the amount of information given by "removing" this uncertainty, i.e., by answering the question of which event of the given space actually occurred. Thus $H_n(X)$ is a measure of the uncertainty in the sequence $x_0, \cdots, x_{n-1}$. The quantity $H_{nY}(X)$ is a measure of the average amount of uncertainty in the same sequence $x_0, \cdots, x_{n-1}$, given that this sequence entered the channel and that the sequence $y_0, \cdots, y_{n-1}$ was obtained at the output. Thus $H_{nY}(X)$ indicates how much uncertainty still remains in the sequence $x_0, \cdots, x_{n-1}$ after it has been transmitted through the channel. Of course, we always have $H_{nY}(X) = 0$ for a noiseless channel, for then knowledge of the received sequence $y_0, \cdots, y_{n-1}$ tells us with certainty the transmitted sequence $x_0, \cdots, x_{n-1}$. In the general case, $H_{nY}(X) > 0$ and represents the *"residual entropy"* of the sequence $x_0, \cdots, x_{n-1}$, which it retains after passing through the channel. After dividing $H_n(X)$ and $H_{nY}(X)$ by n and passing to the limit as $n \to \infty$, we obtain $H(X)$, the average uncertainty per signal of the source $[A, \mu]$, and $H_Y(X)$, the average uncertainty per signal of the source after the message has passed through the channel.

On the other hand, $H_n(x)$ is the amount of information contained in the sequence $x_0, \cdots, x_{n-1}$, and $H_{nY}(X)$ is the amount of information it retains after being transmitted through the channel. The difference $H_n(X) - H_{nY}(X)$ is thus a measure of the average amount of information given by a sequence $x_0, \cdots, x_{n-1}$ transmitted through the channel. After dividing by n and passing to the limit, we find that the difference $H(X) - H_Y(X)$ is the amount of information obtained on the average when a signal of the source $[A, \mu]$ is transmitted through the channel. This quantity

$$R(X, Y) = H(X) - H_Y(X)$$

is therefore the most important characteristic of the quality of transmission. It is natural to call it the *rate* of transmission of information from the given source $[A, \mu]$ through the channel $[A, \nu_x, B]$. We have by (10.3)

$$H_Y(X) = H(X, Y) - H(Y),$$

which means that

$$R(X, Y) = H(X) + H(Y) - H(X, Y).$$

Thus the rate of transmission $R(X, Y)$ is uniquely determined by giving the entropy of the three sources $[A, \mu]$, $[B, \eta]$, and $[C, \omega]$.

#11. The ergodic case

Retaining the terminology and notation of the preceding sections, we now assume that the source $[A, \mu]$ is ergodic and that the channel $[A, \nu_x, B]$ has finite memory m. We shall now show that in this case the compound source $[C, \omega]$ and the source $[B, \eta]$ at the channel output are also ergodic.

Let Z be any cylinder of the space C^I, obtained by fixing any sequence of pairs $(x_0, y_0), \cdots, (x_{j-1}, y_{j-1})$ or, equivalently, the pair of sequences

$$u = x_0, \cdots, x_{j-1}; \quad v = y_0, \cdots, y_{j-1}.$$

The sequences u and v (equivalently, the cylinder Z) will be regarded as constant throughout the proof. Now consider any fixed m-term sequence $z = x_{-m}, \cdots, x_{-1}$, and denote by w the sequence $x_{-m} \cdots x_{-1} x_0 \cdots x_{j-1}$ of constant length $m + j = t$. Since the source $[A, \mu]$ is ergodic, we have almost everywhere in A^I

$$(11.1) \qquad \lim_{n \to \infty} \frac{1}{n} \sum_{k=0}^{n-1} g_w(T^k x) = \mu(w).$$

Furthermore, by Birkhoff's theorem, the limit

$$(11.2) \qquad \lim_{s \to \infty} \frac{1}{s} \sum_{l=0}^{s-1} g_w(T^{r+lt} x) = \psi_{r,z}(x)$$

exists almost everywhere in A^I for $0 \leq r \leq t-1$, and for any sequence z. Let us denote by $M \subset A^I$ the set of x for which (11.1) obtains and for which the limits (11.2) exist for any r $(0 \leq r \leq t-1)$ and z. Obviously $\mu(M) = 1$.

The sum on the left side of (11.2)

$$(11.3) \qquad \sum_{l=0}^{s-1} g_w(T^{r+lt} x)$$

is clearly the number of values of l $(0 \leq l \leq s-1)$ for which $T^{r+lt}x \in w$, i.e., for which the sequence of length t

$$c_l = x_{r+lt-m}, \cdots, x_{r+lt+j-1}$$

coincides with the sequence w. (We note that the sequences c_l fill the sequence $x_{r-m}, \cdots, x_{r-m+st-1}$ without gaps and without overlapping, as l runs through the values $0, 1, \cdots, s-1$.) Let this number be denoted by

$$p = p(s, r, z, x),$$

where, by (11.2), for any $x \in M$

(11.4) $p = s\psi_{r,z}(x) + o(s)$

as $s \to \infty$, and let $l_1, l_2, \cdots, l_p$, in order of increasing size, denote the values of l $(0 \leq l \leq s-1)$ for which c_l coincides with w. Furthermore, let γ_l $(0 \leq l \leq s-1)$ denote the (random) sequence

$$y_{r+lt}, \cdots, y_{r+lt+j-1}$$

of length j.

The sequences γ_{l_k} $(1 \leq k \leq p)$ are of special interest to us. Let A_k denote the event consisting of the sequence γ_{l_k} coinciding with the sequence v (which enters into the definition of the cylinder Z); obviously A_k is the event (cylinder) $T^{r+l_k t}v$ of the space B^r. Its probability for a given x is $\nu_x(A_k) = \nu_x(T^{r+l_k t}v)$. But our channel is without anticipation and has finite memory m. Therefore the event A_k determined by the sequence γ_{l_k} depends statistically only on

$$x_{r+l_k t-m}, \cdots, x_{r+l_k t+j-1},$$

i.e., on the sequence c_{l_k} to which x belongs. But, by the definition of the number l_k we have, for $k=1,2,\cdots,p$

$$c_{l_k} = T^{r+l_k t}w.$$

Thus we arrive at the conclusion that the probability $\nu_x(T^{r+l_kt}v)$ has the same value for all $x \in T^{r+l_kt}w$. Since our channel is stationary, this probability is the same as the probability $\nu_x(v)$ of the cylinder v for any $x \in w$. This latter probability, which it is convenient to denote by $\nu_w(v)$, is independent of either k or r.

It follows that $\nu_x(A_k) = \nu_w(v)$ for all k $(1 \leq k \leq p)$. Moreover, it is an immediate consequence of the fact that the channel memory is m that the events A_k are independent. We have $p \to \infty$ as $s \to \infty$ (if $x \in M$), so that the events $A_1, \cdots, A_p$ form a classical Bernouilli scheme. All these events are defined in the space B^I. If q denotes the number of values of k $(1 \leq k \leq p)$ for which A_k occurs (for a given $x \in M$), then, as $s \to \infty$ (which, for $x \in M$, implies $p \to \infty$), we have by the strong law of large numbers

$$(11.5) \qquad \frac{q}{p} \to \nu_w(v)$$

with probability 1. This means that if $x \in M$ and if N denotes the set of values of $y \in B$ for which (11.5) holds as $s \to \infty$, then $\nu_x(N) = 1$. The set N depends on r, z, and x, i.e., $N = N(r,z,x)$, but r and z can assume only a finite number of different values. If we put

$$\prod_{r,z} N(r,z,x) = N_x^*$$

then obviously for $x \in M$

$$\nu_x(N_x^*) = 1,$$

and (11.5) holds for any r and z, if $x \in M$, $y \in N_x^*$. But since by (11.4)

$$\frac{p}{s} \to \psi_{r,z}(x) \quad (s \to \infty)$$

for any $x \in M$, then, for $x \in M$, $y \in N_x^*$, we obtain

$$(11.6) \qquad \frac{q}{s} \to \nu_w(v) \, \psi_{r_1 z}(x) \quad (s \to \infty)$$

for any r and z.

By the definition of the number q, we have immediately

$$q = \sum_{l=0}^{s-1} g_w(T^{r+lt}x) \, g_v(T^{r+lt}y)$$

Summing this expression over r from 0 to $t-1$, we find, for $x \in M$, $y \in N_x^*$, using (11.6)

$$\sum_{k=0}^{st-1} g_w(T^k x) \, g_v(T^k y) = s\nu_w(v) \sum_{r=0}^{t-1} \psi_{r,z}(x) + o(s).$$

But by the definition of the function $\psi_{r,z}(x)$ and by the ergodicity of the source $[A, \mu]$, we have, for $x \in M$

$$\sum_{r=0}^{t-1} \psi_{r,z}(x) = \lim_{s \to \infty} \frac{1}{s} \sum_{k=0}^{st-1} g_w(T^k x) = t\mu(w),$$

so that

$$(11.7) \qquad \sum_{k=0}^{st-1} g_w(T^k x) \, g_v(T^k y) = st\mu(w) \, \nu_w(v) + o(s)$$

for $x \in M$, $y \in N_x^*$.

Now we sum (11.7) over all possible sequences z. In doing so, we recall that w is a sequence of the type $x_{-m}, \cdots, x_{-1}$, $x_0, \cdots, x_{j-1}$, where $x_{-m}, \cdots, x_{-1}$ is now the variable sequence z, and $x_0, \cdots, x_{j-1}$ is the fixed sequence u. Therefore $\sum_z w = u$ and $\sum_z \omega(w,v) = \omega(u,v) = \omega(Z)$. Since $\mu(w)\nu_w(v) = \omega(w,v)$ by the very definition of the distribution ω, the right side of (11.7) becomes

$$st\omega(u,v) + o(s) = st\omega(Z) + o(s)$$

after summation over z. The sum of the terms in the left side of (11.7) can be written

$$\sum_{k=0}^{st-1} g_v(T^k y) \sum_z g_w(T^k x).$$

Since $\sum_z w = u$, the inner sum equals $g_u(T^k x)$; therefore, summing the left side of (11.7) over z gives

$$\sum_{k=0}^{st-1} g_u(T^k x)\, g_v(T^k y),$$

and we obtain for $x \in M$, $y \in N_x^*$

(11.8) $$\sum_{k=0}^{st-1} g_Z(T^k x,\, T^k y) = st\omega(Z) + o(s).$$

If Q is the set of pairs (x,y) for which $x \in M$, $y \in N_x^*$, then by definition of the distribution ω, and because $\nu_x(N_x^*) = 1$, we have

$$\omega(Q) = \int_M \nu_x(N_x^*)\, d\mu(x) = \mu(M) = 1.$$

Thus (11.8) obtains almost everywhere in C^I. This means that the source $[C, \omega]$ reflects the cylinder Z. Since this cylinder is arbitrary, then by the theorem of #4, we have proved that the source $[C, \omega]$ is ergodic.

It follows at once that the source $[B; \eta]$ is ergodic. Indeed, if $N \in F_B$ is an invariant set in B^I, then $A^I \times N$ is obviously an invariant set in C^I. Since the source $[C, \omega]$ has already been proved to be ergodic, then $\eta(N) = \omega(A^I \times N)$ equals 0 or 1; but this means that the source $[B, \eta]$ is ergodic.

CHAPTER IV.

Feinstein's Fundamental Lemma

#12. Formulation of the problem

The authors of most investigations on the foundations of information theory agree in considering the culmination of the theory of discrete information to be Shannon's theorems on the optimum use that can be made of noisy channels by suitably coding the transmitted text. The proofs of these theorems are given only sketchily in Shannon's works, the analysis being limited to sources of the Markov chain type. In his work, McMillan considerably refined in mathematical respects the fundamental concepts of Shannon's theory. (It is just these refined concepts that we used in the preceding sections.) Moreover, he outlined a method of proving Shannon's theorems for any ergodic source; more exactly, he tried to carry over to this case a proof the idea of which had been given by Shannon. In this connection, a number of gaps were discovered, which evidently can not be filled even in the special case of the Markov sources considered by Shannon.

In 1953, Feinstein [4] proposed a fundamentally new way of substantiating Shannon's theorems, which makes the whole theory considerably more transparent. Feinstein's idea consists in deriving from the channel itself as much as can possibly be used to prove Shannon's theorems, before coding and even before connecting the channel to any particular source. This is done by proving a proposition which it is natural to call the fundamental lemma of the whole theory, and which is formulated without any mention of either sources or codes. The proof of this proposition is our next problem. It should be noted that Feinstein carries out the proof only for channels without memory ($m=0$) and only alludes to possible generalizations. It is, of course, very important to know to how broad a class of channels the fundamental lemma applies. We also note that both the statement and the proof of the lemma as given by Feinstein contain a number of inaccuracies which, however, can be corrected easily.

Consider a stationary channel $[A, \nu_x, B]$, without anticipation and with finite memory m. If this channel is fed by a stationary source $[A, \mu]$, we obtain a definite rate of transmission

$$R(X, Y) = H(X) - H_Y(X),$$

which (see ♯10) can be regarded as the amount of information obtained on the average when one letter is transmitted. Of course, this rate depends on the source A, driving the channel. However, the least upper bound of $R(X, Y)$ for all possible *ergodic* sources $[A, \mu]$ is a quantity which depends only on the channel $[A, \nu_x, B]$ itself. We shall denote this quantity by C, and we shall call it the (ergodic) *capacity* of the channel.

As before, we denote the elements of the sets A^I and B^I by

$$x = \cdots, x_{-1}, x_0, x_1 \cdots \text{ and } y = \cdots y_{-1}, y_0, y_1, \cdots,$$

respectively. Let n be any fixed positive integer. Let us agree to denote by u the sequence (cylinder $x_{-m}, \cdots, x_{-1}, x_0, \cdots, x_{n-1}$ of length $n+m$, where all the x_i take on definite values (letters of the alphabet A). Obviously, the number of different sequences u is a^{m+n}, where a is the number of letters in the alphabet A. Similarly, let us denote by v the sequence (cylinder) $y_0, \cdots, y_{n-1}$ of length n, where all the y_i

are letters of the alphabet B. Obviously, the number of different sequences v is b^n, where b is the number of letters in the alphabet B. Since the memory of the channel is m, then the probability $\nu_x(v)$ of receiving $y \in v$ at the channel output when a given x is transmitted is the same for all x belonging to the same sequence u. Thus, this probability depends only on the sequences u and v selected, and it is natural to denote it by $\nu_u(v)$. Similarly, if V is the union of several sequences v, we shall denote by $\nu_u(V)$ the probability of the event $y \in V$ when any $x \in u$ is transmitted.

Now, let λ be any constant $\left(0 < \lambda < \dfrac{1}{2}\right)$. Let us agree to call a group $\{u_i\}$ $(1 \leq i \leq N)$ of u-sequences *distinguishable* if there exists a group $\{V_i\}$ $(1 \leq i \leq N)$ of sets $V_i \subset B^I$ where each V_i $(1 \leq i \leq N)$ is a set of several sequences v, such that 1) V_i and V_k have no sequences in common for $i \neq k$, and 2) $\nu_{u_i}(V_i) > 1 - \lambda$ $(1 \leq i \leq N)$. Clearly, this definition of a distinguishable group depends on the parameter λ. We can now formulate Feinstein's fundamental lemma as follows.

Lemma.

If a given channel is stationary, without anticipation, and with finite memory m, then, for sufficiently small $\lambda > 0$ and sufficiently large n, there exists a distinguishable group $\{u_i\}$ $(1 \leq i \leq N)$ of u-sequences with

$$N > 2^{n(C-\lambda)}$$

members, where C is the (ergodic) capacity of the channel.

The importance of a proposition of this kind in evaluating the optimum transmission of information is clear almost immediately. If λ is small, since $\nu_{u_i}(V_i) > 1 - \lambda$, when a sequence u_i is transmitted, then at the channel output we obtain with overwhelming probability a sequence v in the group V_i; since the groups V_i have no v in common, then, knowing v, we uniquely determine the group V_i which contains it, which means that we guess with an overwhelming probability the transmitted sequence u_i. Of course all this is under the condition that the group $\{u_i\}$ is distinguishable. Thus, if only sequences of a certain distinguishable group are used to send signals, then, despite the noise, the signals sent can be guessed with overwhelming probability. The question of whether any text suitable for transmission can be "encoded" into the sequences u_i depends, of course, on how many such sequences there are in the first place. The fundamental lemma shows at once that the number of such sequences is very great for sufficiently large n. After this lemma has been proved, we shall consider the question of how to use the estimate of N that it affords to compute an index of optimum transmission of given material through a given channel. In fact, this is the way we shall approach the basic Shannon theorems.

#13. Proof of the lemma

We shall divide the proof into a number of separate steps in the interest of a better presentation.

1. *The source* $[A, \mu]$. By definition of the number C, we can find an ergodic source $[A, \mu]$ for the channel $[A, \nu_x, B]$ such that when this source drives the channel, we have a rate of transmission (see the end of #10)

$$R(X, Y) = H(X) - H_Y(X) > C - \frac{\lambda}{4}.$$

Here $H(X)$ denotes the entropy of the source $[A, \mu]$ and $H_Y(X)$ the average conditional entropy of the same source, given the signal received at the channel output. The source $[A, \mu]$, being ergodic, has the E property according to McMillan's theorem (see #5). This means the following. Let w denote an arbitrary sequence $x_0, \cdots, x_{n-1}$ of letters from the alphabet A (w is therefore some cylinder in A^I). Moreover, let $W_0 \subset A^I$ denote the set (union) of all cylinders w for which

$$(13.1) \qquad \left| \frac{\lg \mu(w)}{n} + H(X) \right| \leq \frac{\lambda}{4};$$

then, for arbitrarily small $\lambda > 0$ we have for sufficiently large n

$$\mu(W_0) > 1 - \lambda.$$

2. *The source* $[C, \omega]$. Connecting the source $[A, \mu]$ to the channel $[A, \nu_x, B]$ gives us according to the definitions of #10 the *compound* source $[C, \omega]$, with the alphabet $C = A \times B$ and entropy $H(X, Y)$. By the theorems of #11, this source is ergodic, and therefore, by McMillan's theorem (#5) has the E property. This means the following. Each pair (w, v) of n-term sequences $[w \subset A^I, v \subset B^I]$ is some cylinder in the space C^I, with a definite probability $\omega(w, v)$ in this space. Let Z denote the set of all cylinders (w, v) for which

$$(13.2) \qquad \left| \frac{\lg \omega(w, v)}{n} + H(X, Y) \right| \leq \frac{\lambda}{4};$$

then, for arbitrarily small $\lambda > 0$ and $\delta > 0$, we have, for sufficiently large n

$$\omega(Z) > 1 - \delta.$$

3. *The source* $[B, \eta]$. This source, which we described in #10, is determined by the relation

$$\eta(M) = \int_{A^I} \nu_x(M) \, d\mu(x) = \omega(A^I \times M) \quad (M \in F_B).$$

We proved that it is ergodic at the end of #11. According to McMillan's theorem it has the E property. This means the following. The probability of the set of n-term sequences $v \subset B^I$ for which

$$(13.3) \qquad \left| \frac{\lg \eta(v)}{n} + H(Y) \right| \leq \frac{\lambda}{4}$$

is as close to 1 as desired for sufficiently large n. ($H(Y)$ denotes the entropy of the source $[B, \eta]$.)

4. *The set A_w and its probability.* Let us denote by X the set of pairs of sequences (w, v) for which the inequalities (13.2) and (13.3) are satisfied. By the foregoing, we have

$$\omega(X) > 1 - \frac{1}{2}\lambda^2,$$

if n is large enough. Now, for any sequence w, let $A_w \subset B^I$ denote the set of all sequences v for which $(w, v) \in X$, i.e., for which the inequalities (13.2) and (13.3) are satisfied. Furthermore, let $W_1 \subset A^I$ denote the set of all sequences $w \subset W_0$ for which

$$(13.4) \qquad \frac{\omega(w, A_w)}{\mu(w)} = \frac{\omega(w, A_w)}{\omega(w, B^I)} > 1 - \frac{\lambda}{2} \ .$$

We now estimate the probability of the set W_1 by using Lemma 2.1. The roles of the spaces A, B, AB are played by the sets of all sequences w, v, (w, v), respectively. For Z we take the set X, for U_0 the set W_0. Then clearly $\frac{1}{2}\lambda^2$ plays the role of δ_1 and λ that of δ_2. The set of sequences v for which $(w, v) \notin X$, i.e., $\Gamma_w = B^I - A_w$, takes the place of the set Γ_w. Finally, the set of $w \subset W_0$ for which the conditional probability

$$P_w(\Gamma_w) = 1 - P_w(A_w) = 1 - \frac{\omega(w, A_w)}{\mu(W)} \leq \alpha$$

plays the role of the set U_1. Putting $\alpha = \frac{\lambda}{2}$, we can take our set W_1 as the set U_1 of Lemma 2.1. We see at once that all the premises of Lemma 2.1 have been fulfilled. Using it, we conclude that

(13.5) $\mu(W_1) > 1 - \lambda - \lambda = 1 - 2\lambda.$

Now let the sequence w belong to the set W_1 and the sequence v to the set A_w, so that by the definition of the set A_w we have $(w, v) \subset X$. Since $W_1 \subset W_0$, then, by the definition of the sets X and W_0, all three inequalities (13.1), (13.2), (13.3) are fulfilled for the pairs (w, v). In particular, we have

$$\frac{\lg \mu(w)}{n} + H(X) \leq \frac{\lambda}{4}; \qquad \frac{\lg \eta(v)}{n} + H(Y) \leq \frac{\lambda}{4};$$

$$\frac{\lg \omega(w, v)}{n} + H(X, Y) \geq -\frac{\lambda}{4},$$

whence

$$\lg \frac{\omega(w, v)}{\mu(w)\eta(v)} + n[H(X, Y) - H(X) - H(Y)] \geq -\frac{3}{4} n\lambda.$$

Since (see #10)

$$H(X) + H(Y) - H(X, Y) = R(X, Y),$$

we find

$$\lg \frac{\omega(w, v)}{\mu(w)\eta(v)} \geq n\left[R(X, Y) - \frac{3}{4}\lambda\right],$$

and therefore

$$\frac{\omega(w, v)}{\mu(w)} \geq 2^{n[R(X, Y) - \frac{3}{4}\lambda]}\eta(v).$$

Since we have $R(X, Y) > C - \dfrac{\lambda}{4}$ by the choice of the source $[A, \mu]$, then

$$\frac{\omega(w, v)}{\mu(w)} > 2^{n(C-\lambda)} \eta(v).$$

This inequality holds for any $w \subset W_1$, $v \subset A_w$. Keeping the sequence $w \subset W_1$ fixed, and summing over all $v \subset A_w$, we find

$$\frac{\omega(w, A_w)}{\mu(w)} > 2^{n(C-\lambda)} \eta(A_w),$$

but the left side of this inequality does not exceed unity, since $\omega(w, A_w) \leq \omega(w, B^I) = \mu(w)$. Therefore we find that for any sequence $w \subset W_1$

(13.6) $\qquad\qquad\qquad \eta(A_w) < 2^{-n(C-\lambda)}.$

5. *Special groups of w-sequences.* We agree to call the group $\{w_i\}(1 \leq i \leq N)$ of w-sequence *special* if a set B_i of v-sequences can be associated with each sequence w_i of this group such that

1) the sets B_i and B_k have no common sequence for $i \neq k$;

2) $\dfrac{\omega(w_i, B_i)}{\mu(w_i)} > 1 - \lambda \quad (1 \leq i \leq N)$;

3) $\eta(B_i) < 2^{-n(C-\lambda)} \quad (1 \leq i \leq N)$.

First of all, let us convince ourselves that *special* groups exist. To do this, we take any sequence $w \subset W_1$ and put $B = A_w$. Then by (13.4) and (13.6), we have

$$\frac{\omega(w, B)}{\mu(w)} > 1 - \lambda; \ \eta(B) \leq 2^{-n(C-\lambda)}.$$

Therefore, every sequence $w \subset W_1$ is a special group, which proves the existence of special groups. Now let us call a special group of *w*-sequences *maximal*, if adding any other sequence to it causes it to lose the character of a special group.[*] In view of the foregoing, the existence of a maximal group is obvious.

6. *Estimate of the number of members of a maximal special group.* Let $M = \{w_i\}$ $(1 \leq i \leq N)$ be a maximal special group of *w*-sequences. Now, for any sequence *w*, let us put

$$A_w - A_w \sum_{i=1}^{N} B_i = B_w.$$

Obviously the set $B_w \subset B^I$ has no elements in common with any of the sets B_i $(1 \leq i \leq N)$. If $w \subset W_1$, then by (13.6)

$$\eta(B_w) \leq \eta(A_w) < 2^{-n(C-\lambda)}.$$

If the sequence $w \subset W_1$ did not belong to the group M and if we had at the same time

$$\frac{\omega(w, B_w)}{\mu(w)} > 1 - \lambda,$$

then adding this sequence *w* to the group M would evidently again give a special group of *w*-sequences, which is impossible, since the group M is assumed to be maximal. Therefore, if $w \subset W_1$ and $w \notin M$ (i.e., if $w \subset W_1 - MW_1$), then

$$(13.7) \qquad \frac{\omega(w, B_w)}{\mu(w)} \leq 1 - \lambda.$$

But by the definition of the set B_w

$$\omega(w, B_w) = \omega(w, A_w) - \omega\left(w, A_w \sum_{i=1}^{N} B_i\right),$$

and if $w \subset W_1 - MW_1$, it follows from (13.4) and (13.7) that

---

[*] If the set of *all* *w*-sequences is a special group, then we consider this group to be maximal also.

$$\omega\left(w, A_w \sum_{i=1}^{N} B_i\right) = \omega(w, A_w) - \omega(w, B_w) >$$

$$> \left(1 - \frac{\lambda}{2}\right)\mu(w) - (1-\lambda)\mu(w) = \frac{\lambda}{2}\mu(w).$$

From this we find that

(13.8)
$$\eta\left(\sum_{i=1}^{N} B_i\right) = \omega\left(A^I, \sum_{i=1}^{N} B_i\right) \geqq \omega\left(W_1, \sum_{i=1}^{N} B_i\right)$$

$$= \omega\left(W_1 - MW_1, \sum_{i=1}^{N} B_i\right) + \omega\left(MW_1, \sum_{i=1}^{N} B_i\right)$$

$$= \sum_{w \subset W_1 - MW_1} \omega\left(w, \sum_{i=1}^{N} B_i\right) + \sum_{w \subset MW_1} \omega\left(w, \sum_{i=1}^{N} B_i\right)$$

$$> \frac{\lambda}{2} \sum_{w \subset W_1 - MW_1} \mu(w) + \sum_{w \subset MW_1} \omega\left(w, \sum_{i=1}^{N} \bar{B}_i\right)$$

$$\geqq \frac{\lambda}{2}\left[\mu(W_1) - \mu(MW_1)\right] + (1-\lambda)\mu(MW_1),$$

where only the estimate of the last sum requires explanation. The fact is that if $w \subset MW_1 \subset M$, the sequence w is one of the sequences w_i of the special group M. For example, if $w = w_k$ then

$$\omega\left(w, \sum_{i=1}^{N} B_i\right) \geqq \omega(w_k, B_k) > (1-\lambda)\,\mu(w),$$

and therefore

$$\sum_{w \subset MW_1} \omega\left(w, \sum_{i=1}^{N} B_i\right) > (1-\lambda)\,\mu(MW_1).$$

Furthermore, using (13.5) we find that for $\lambda \leqq \frac{1}{2}$, (13.8) becomes

(13.9)
$$\eta\left(\sum_{i=1}^{N} B_i\right) \geqq \frac{\lambda}{2}\mu(W_1) + \left(1 - \lambda - \frac{\lambda}{2}\right)\mu(MW_1)$$

$$\geqq \frac{\lambda}{2}\mu(W_1) > \frac{\lambda}{2}\,(1-2\lambda) = \gamma.$$

But since by the definition of a *special* group

$$\eta(B_i) < 2^{-n(C-\lambda)} \quad (1 \leqq i \leqq N),$$

then, on the other hand

$$\eta\left(\sum_{i=1}^{N} B_i\right) < N \cdot 2^{-n(C-\lambda)}.$$

Comparing this with the inequality (13.9) we find

$$N > \gamma 2^{n(C-\lambda)},$$

and therefore, for sufficiently large n

$$N > 2^{n(C-2\lambda)}.$$

Thus we have established an important lower bound for the number of terms in any maximal special group of w-sequences.

7. *Completion of the proof of the fundamental lemma.* Let us consider an arbitrary maximal special group $\{w_i\}$ $(1 \leq i \leq N)$ of w-sequences, and let us extend each sequence w_i of this group by adding m more letters to the left, obtaining in this way a new sequence u_i of length $n+m$. Let us convince ourselves that by selecting this extension in a suitable way, we have

$$\frac{\omega(u_i, B_i)}{\mu(u_i)} > 1 - \lambda \quad (1 \leq i \leq N).$$

Every possible extension of the sequence w_i by m letters to the left gives a cylinder (sequence) u_i contained in the cylinder w_i $(u_i \subset w_i)$, and the union of all the cylinders $u_i \subset w_i$ is the cylinder w_i. Therefore for $1 \leq i \leq N$

$$\frac{\omega(w_i, B_i)}{\mu(w_i)} = \sum_{u_i \subset w_i} \frac{\omega(u_i, B_i)}{\mu(w_i)} = \sum_{u_i \subset w_i} \frac{\omega(u_i, B_i)}{\mu(u_i)} \frac{\mu(u_i)}{\mu(w_i)}.$$

The left side of this equality exceeds $1-\lambda$ by the definition of a special group. The sum of the second factors in the sum on the right side is obviously unity. Therefore at least one of the first factors must exceed $1-\lambda$; but this means that, for at least one extension, we must have

(13.10) $$\frac{w(u_i, B_i)}{\mu(u_i)} > 1-\lambda,$$

as asserted.

By the definition of the distribution ω

$$\omega(u_i, B_i) = \int_{u_i} \nu_x(B_i)\, d\mu(x).$$

But, as we saw in #12, $\nu_x(B_i)$ assumes the same value for all $x \in u_i$, which we agreed to denote by $\nu_{u_i}(B_i)$. Thus

$$\omega(u_i, B_i) = \mu(u_i)\nu_{u_i}(B_i).$$

and (13.10) can be written as

$$\nu_{u_i}(B_i) > 1-\lambda \quad (1 \leq i \leq N).$$

Selecting the extension of the sequence w_i in the manner indicated above, we obtain a group of N sequences u_i of length $n+m$ (of letters from the alphabet A) and a group of N sets B_i, each of which is the union of several sequences v of length n (of letters from the alphabet B), where 1) the sets B_i and B_k have no common elements for $i \neq k$, 2) $\nu_{u_i}(B_i) > 1-\lambda (1 \leq i \leq N)$, and 3) $N > 2^{n(C-2\lambda)}$. This just means that the sequences u_i $(1 \leq i \leq N)$ form a distinguishable group. But since the number of terms of this group exceeds $2^{n(C-2\lambda)}$ and $\lambda > 0$ can be chosen as small as desired, the proof of the fundamental lemma is complete.

CHAPTER V.

Shannon's Theorems

#14. Coding

Up to now, we have always assumed that the source feeding the given channel has an alphabet which is identical with the input alphabet of the channel. However, in practice these alphabets are different in the majority of cases, and we must now consider the general case.

Suppose the output of the stationary source $[A_0, \mu]$ is to be transmitted by means of the stationary channel $[A, \nu_x, B]$ where in general the alphabets A_0 and A are different. Then, before transmitting, it is necessary to transform ("*encode*") the sequence of letters from the alphabet A_0 emanating from the source into some sequence of letters from the alphabet A. As usual, we suppose that any message emanating from the source $[A_0, \mu]$ is in the form of a sequence

$$(14.1) \qquad \theta = \cdots, \theta_{-1}, \theta_0, \theta_1, \cdots,$$

where all the θ_i are letters of the alphabet A_0. We uniquely transform ("encode") each θ into some sequence

$$(14.2) \qquad x = \cdots, x_{-1}, x_0, x_1, \cdots,$$

where all the x_i are letters of the alphabet A. The rules of this transformation constitute the "code" used. Thus, from the mathematical point of view, a code is simply any function

$$x = x(\theta),$$

where $\theta \in A_0^I$, $x \in A^I$. It is clear that formally every code can be regarded as a kind of channel with input alphabet A_0 and output alphabet A. Such channels are characterized as being noiseless, i.e., to a sequence θ at the channel input corresponds a unique sequence $x = x(\theta)$ at the output. We can give this channel the usual designation $[A_0, \rho_0, A]$, where the form of the function $\rho_0(M)$ ($M \in A'$) is also apparent, namely

$$\rho_0(M) = \begin{cases} 1 & [x(\theta) \in M] \\ 0 & [x(\theta) \notin M]. \end{cases}$$

However, not every code has practical value. If we must actually know (as will be necessary in the general case) the whole sequence θ, i.e., the whole infinite message from the source $[A_0, \mu]$ in order to determine any letter x_k of the encoded text, then obviously, in practice, we can never determine this letter. Consequently, the only codes of importance in applications are those such that it suffices to know some finite sequence of letters $\theta_k \in A_0$ in order to uniquely determine each letter $x_k \in A$ (and also each finite sequence of such letters). In particular, in information theory "sequential coding", is used predominantly, which consists of the following: Both the sequences (14.1) and (14.2) are divided into finite subsequences of any length which are numbered from left to right, just like the letters of these sequences. A rule is given which uniquely determines the k'th subsequence of the sequence x in terms of the k'th subsequence of the sequence θ.

Now let us turn to the problem of transmitting the output of the source $[A_0, \mu]$ by means of the channel $[A, \nu_x, B]$. We code each message θ of the source $[A_0, \mu]$ into some specific message x, composed of letters from the alphabet A. We then pass this x through the channel $[A, \nu_x, B]$ and obtain some message $y \in B^I$ at its output. Obviously, the result of connecting the code selected to the channel $[A, \nu_x, B]$ can be regàrded as a new channel $[A_0, \lambda_\theta, B]$. It is very easy to determine the function (probability) $\lambda_\theta(Q)$ $(Q \in F_B)$. Since the coding transforms the message $\theta \in A_0^I$ into the message $x(\theta) \in A^I$, the probability $\lambda_\theta(Q)$ of obtaining $y \in Q$ for a given θ is the probability of obtaining $y \in Q$ if the message $x = x(\theta)$ enters the input of the channel $[A, \nu_x, B]$, i.e.

$$\lambda_\theta(Q) = \nu_{x(\theta)}(Q),$$

and the channel $[A_0, \lambda_\theta, B]$ can be written as $[A_0, \nu_{x(\theta)}, B]$.

The process which we are examining consists in connecting the source $[A_0, \mu]$ to this new channel $[A_0, \lambda_\theta, B]$; this time the source alphabet coincides with the channel input alphabet, so that we have a situation with which we are familiar. In particular, connecting the source to the channel gives, as we know, the "compound" source $[C, \omega]$ where $C = A \times B$, and where the probability distribution is such that for $M \in F_{A_0}$, $N \in F_B$ we have

$$\omega(M \times N) = \int_M \lambda_\theta(N) \, d\mu(\theta) = \int_M \nu_{x(\theta)}(N) \, d\mu(\theta).$$

#15. The first Shannon theorem

Suppose we have an ergodic source $[A_0, \mu]$ and a stationary, non-anticipating channel $[A, \nu_x, B]$ with finite memory m. Let the entropy of the source $[A_0, \mu]$ be H_0, and let the ergodic capacity of the channel $[A, \nu_x, B]$ be C. We assume that $H_0 < C$, and choose a positive number $\lambda < \dfrac{1}{2}(C - H_0)$. Then we select a particular code which transforms the output of the source $[A_0, \mu]$ into the alphabet A of the given channel.

First of all, we note that the source $[A_0, \mu]$, being ergodic, has the E property (see #5). In particular, this means that for sufficiently large n, the sequences α of letters from the alphabet A_0 can be divided into two groups, a "high probability" group, for each sequence α of which

$$\frac{\lg \mu(\alpha)}{n} + H_0 > -\lambda,$$

or, equivalently

$$\mu(\alpha) > 2^{-n(H_0 + \lambda)},$$

and a "low probability" group, the total probability of which is as small as desired. Obviously the number of sequences in the high probability group is less than $2^{n(H_0 + \lambda)} < 2^{n(C - \lambda)}$. In what follows we shall denote these sequences by $\alpha_1, \alpha_2, \cdots$. We shall denote the set of all sequences in the low probability group by α_0.

Now we turn to the channel $[A, \nu_x, B]$. By the fundamental lemma of Chapter IV, for sufficiently large n there exists a distinguishable group $\{u_i\}$ $(1 \leq i \leq N)$ of sequences u of length $n + m$ (consisting of letters from the alphabet A), with $N > 2^{n(C - \lambda)}$ members. Thus, since N is larger than the number of sequences α_i in the high probability group just considered, we can associate with each sequence α_i a sequence u_i such that different u_i correspond to different α_i. In doing this, at least one sequence of the distinguishable group has not been used; we associate this sequence with all the sequences α_0 of the low probability group. After doing this, to each n-term sequence α of letters from the alphabet A_0 corresponds a specific sequence u of length $n+m$ from the alphabet A, a sequence which belongs to the distinguishable group $\{u_i\}$.

We now divide the sequence θ of letters from the alphabet A_0, which is to be coded, into subsequences of length n, and the sequence x, into which θ is to be encoded, into subsequences of length $n+m$. We number both sets of subsequences from left to right, as usual. The k'th subsequence in the message θ will be one of the sequences α; then we select as the k'th subsequence in the message x, the sequence u_i of our distinguishable group which corresponds to this sequence α. Doing this for all k $(-\infty < k < +\infty)$, it is clear that we uniquely determine $x = x(\theta)$ in terms of the given θ. In this way we have set up a specific code, which we shall retain in all that follows. Obviously, this code is an example of the "sequential coding" discussed in #14.

Connecting the code just selected to the channel $[A, \nu_x, B]$ we obtain, as we saw in #14, a new channel $[A_0, \lambda_\theta, B]$, where we have $\lambda_\theta(Q) = \nu_{x(\theta)}(Q)$ for $Q \in F_B$. Making the source $[A_0, \mu]$ feed this new channel, we arrive, according to #14, at the "compound" source $[C, \omega]$, where $C = A_0 \times B$ and ω $(M \times N)$ (where $M \in F_{A_0}$, $N \in F_B$) is given by the last formula of #14. Let us agree to denote the different sequences of length n, consisting of letters from the alphabet B, by β_k $(k = 1, 2, \cdots)$. Then, by the definition of the distribution ω, we have for any $k \geq 1$ and $i = 0, 1, \cdots, N$

$$\omega(\alpha_i \times \beta_k) = \int_{\alpha_i} \lambda_\theta(\beta_k)\, d\mu(\theta) = \int_{\alpha_i} \nu_{x(\theta)}(\beta_k)\, d\mu(\theta).$$

But $\theta \in \alpha_i$ is equivalent to $x(\theta) \in u_i^*$, and since $\nu_x(\beta_k)$ assumes

---

* Here u_0 is understood to be the sequence of the distinguishable group $\{u_i\}$ into which the whole "low probability group" α_0 is encoded.

the same value for all $x \in u_i$, which we agreed in #12 to designate by $\nu_{u_i}(\beta_k)$, then we have $\nu_{x(\theta)}(\beta_k) = \nu_{u_i}(\beta_k)$ for all $\theta \in \alpha_i$. Thus we find

(1.51) $\omega(\alpha_i \times \beta_k) = \mu(\alpha_i)\, \nu_{u_i}(\beta_k)$.

In order to avoid any misunderstanding, we recall the meaning of the event $\alpha_i \times \beta_k$, the probability of which is given by (15.1): $\alpha_i \times \beta_k$ denotes the joint event that 1) the n-term sequence transmitted by the source $[A_0, \mu]$ coincides with α_i (if $i > 0$) or belongs to the low probability group (if $i = 0$), and 2) after being transmitted through the channel $[A_{0}, \lambda_0, B]$, the n-term sequence transmitted by the source $[A_0, \mu]$ gives an $n+m$-term sequence of letters from the alphabet B, the last n letters of which are the sequence β_k.

Now let i_k be the value of the subscript i $(0 \leq i \leq N)$ for which the probability $\omega(\alpha_i, \beta_k)^*$ has its greatest value. (If there are several such values i, then we take any of them as i_k). Since the conditional probability of the sequence α_i for a given sequence β_k equals

$$\frac{\omega(\alpha_i, \beta_k)}{\omega(A_0^I, \beta_k)},$$

where the denominator is independent of i, then we can also say α_{i_k} is the sequence α_i which is most probable for a given sequence β_k. Let us set

$$\sum_k \sum_{i \neq i_k} \omega(\alpha_i, B_k) = P.$$

Obviously, we can regard P as *the probability that the sequence α_i at the input of the channel $[A_0, \lambda_0, B]$ will not be the most probable one for a given sequence β_k at the output of the channel.*

---

* $\omega(\alpha_i, \beta_k)$ and $\omega(\alpha_i \times \beta_k)$ have the same meaning.

The sequences u_i, into which we encoded all the sequences α_i form a distinguishable group; this implies the existence of a group $\{B_i\}$ $(1 \leq i \leq n)$ (where every B_i is the union of several sequences β_k) such that 1) $\nu_{u_i}(B_i) > 1 - \lambda$, and 2) B_i and B_j have no sequences in common for $i \neq j$. But summing (15.1) over all $\beta_k \subset B_i$, we find

$$\omega(\alpha_i, \beta_i) = \mu(\alpha_i)\nu_{u_i}(B_i) > (1 - \lambda)\mu(\alpha_i) \quad (0 \leq 1 \leq N).$$

Therefore the conditional probability of obtaining a sequence $\beta_k \subset B_i$ at the output of the channel $[A_0, \lambda_0, B]$, given that we had a sequence α_i at the input of the channel is

$$P_{\alpha_i}(B_i) = \frac{\omega(\alpha_i, B_i)}{\mu(\alpha_i)} > 1 - \lambda \quad (0 \leq i \leq N).$$

Thus we see that the two complete systems of events α_i $(0 \leq i \leq N)$ and β_k $(k = 1, 2, \cdots)$ satisfy all the premises of Lemma 2.2. Using this lemma, we find

$$P \leq \lambda.$$

This important result is the first Shannon theorem, which we can state as follows.

Theorem.

Let there be given 1) *a stationary, non-anticipating channel* $[A, \nu_x, B]$ *with ergodic capacity C and finite memory m, and* 2) *an ergodic source $[A_0, \mu]$ with entropy $H_0 < C$. Let $\varepsilon > 0$. Then, for sufficiently large n, the output of the source $[A_0, \mu]$ can be encoded into the alphabet A in such a way that each sequence α_i of letters from the alphabet A_0 is mapped into a sequence u_i of $n + m$ letters from the alphabet A, and such that if the sequence u_i is transmitted through the given channel, we can determine the transmitted sequence α_i with a probability* *greater than* $1-\varepsilon$ *from the sequence received at the channel output.*

The definition of the sequence α_i entails that we select as α_i the sequence which is most probable, given the n letters last received at the channel output. The first Shannon theorem is often formulated less exactly by saying that for $H_0 < C$ it is always possible to find a code such that the transmitted sequence can be guessed from the received sequence with a probable error which does not exceed an arbitrarily small number ε.

♯16. The second Shannon theorem

We retain, *in toto*, the source $[A_0, \mu]$, the channel $[A, \nu_x, B]$ and the code of the preceding section, and also all the notation introduced there. However, we now consider a new problem pertinent to this whole process, namely, the evaluation of its transmission rate, i.e., the amount of information given on the average by one letter at the channel output. To this end, let us examine first the finite probability space $\alpha_i \beta_k$ ($0 \leqq i \leqq N$, $k = 1, 2, \cdots$), with the distribution $\omega(\alpha_i, \beta_k)$, which was considered in ♯15. We recall that α_i was one of the n-term sequences of the high probability group in the output of the given source for $i \geqq 1$, that α_0 was the whole low probability group of such sequences and that β_k was an n-term sequence of letters from the alphabet B (at the channel output). We denoted by P the quantity

$$P = \sum_k \sum_{i \neq i_k} \omega(\alpha_i, \beta_k),$$

where i_k is the value of the subscript i for which the probability $\omega(\alpha_i, \beta_k)$ is the greatest, and we proved that $P < \lambda$.

It is clear that we find ourselves in a position to apply Lemma

2.3; the spaces $\{\alpha_i\}$ and $\{\beta_k\}$ play the role of the spaces $\{A_i\}$ and $\{B_k\}$ of this lemma, and the number $N+1$ plays the role of the number n. If, as usual, we denote by $H_\beta(\alpha)$ the conditional entropy of the space $\{\alpha_i\}$ for a given β_k, averaged over all β_k, then by Lemma 2.3 we have

$$H_\beta(\alpha) \leq P \lg N - P \lg P - (1-P) \lg (1-P).$$

Here the number N is the number of sequences in the high probability group; as we saw in #15, it does not exceed $2^{n(C-\lambda)} < 2^{nC}$, whence $\lg N < nC$. Taking into account that $P < \lambda$ and that, as is easily seen $-P \lg P - (1-P) \lg (1-P) < 1$ for any P $(0 < P < 1)$, we obtain

$$H_\beta(\alpha) < \lambda nC + 1.$$

In particular, since λ can be chosen arbitrarily small for sufficiently large n, we obtain

$$H_\beta(\alpha) = o(n) \quad (n \to \infty).$$

Here

$$H_\beta(\alpha) = - \sum_k \eta(\beta_k) \sum_{i=0}^{N} f[p_{\beta_k}(\alpha_i)],$$

where

$$f(x) = x \lg x; \quad \eta(\beta_k) = \omega(A^I, \beta_k) \text{ and } p_{\beta_k}(\alpha_i) = \frac{\omega(\alpha_i, \beta_k)}{\omega(A^I, \beta_k)} = \frac{\omega(\alpha_i, \beta_k)}{\eta(\beta_k)}.$$

In all the foregoing α_0, unlike α_i for $i > 0$, denotes not an individual sequence, but the whole "low probability" group of n-term sequences made up of letters from the alphabet A. Now we divide this group into separate sequences

$$\alpha_1', \alpha_2', \cdots, \alpha_q'$$

and instead of the space (α_i) $(0 \leq i \leq N)$ we consider the space

(α_i, α'_j) $(1 \leq i \leq N,\ 1 \leq j \leq q)$ of *all* n-term sequences consisting of letters from the alphabet A_0, with appropriate probabilities $\mu(\alpha_i)$, $\mu(\alpha'_j)$. We leave the space (β_k) as before. Denoting by $H_\beta(\alpha, \alpha')$ the conditional entropy of the space (α_i, α'_j) for a given β_k, averaged over β_k, we find

$$H_\beta(\alpha, \alpha') = -\sum_k \eta(\beta_k)\Big\{ \sum_{i=1}^N f[p_{\beta_k}(\alpha_i)] + \sum_{j=1}^q f[p_{\beta_k}(\alpha'_j)] \Big\}$$

(16.1)

$$= H_\beta(\alpha) + \sum_k \eta(\beta_k)\, f[p_{\beta_k}(\alpha_0)] + R,$$

where

(16.2)
$$R = -\sum_k \eta(\beta_k) \sum_{j=1}^q f[p_{\beta_k}(\alpha'_j)].$$

(In the interest of complete clarity, we note that here

$$p_{\beta_k}(\alpha'_j) = \frac{\omega(\alpha'_j, \beta_k)}{\eta(\beta_k)},$$

where

$$\omega(\alpha'_j, \beta_k) = \int_{\alpha'_j} \lambda_\theta(\beta_k)\, d\mu(\theta).$$

Since $\lambda_\theta(\beta_k)$ has the same value $\lambda_{\alpha_0}(\beta_k)$ for all $\theta \in \alpha'_j \subset \alpha_0$, then

$$p_{\beta_k}(\alpha'_j) = \frac{\lambda_{\alpha_0}(\beta_k)\, \mu(\alpha'_j)}{\eta(\beta_k)}$$

is uniquely given by the data of our problem.)

Since the second term in the right side of (16.1) is negative, then

(16.3)
$$H_\beta(\alpha, \alpha') < H_\beta(\alpha) + R,$$

and since we have already estimated $H_\beta(\alpha)$, it remains only to estimate the quantity R defined by the sum (16.2). Using Lemma 1.1, we find

(16.4)
$$R \leq - \sum_{j=1}^{q} \mu(\alpha'_j) \lg \mu(\alpha'_j),$$

Here, by definition of the low-probability group, we have $\sum_{j=1}^{q} \mu(\alpha'_j) = \mu(\alpha_0) < \lambda$. But it is easily seen that the greatest value of the sum (16.4), under the supplementary condition

$$\sum_{j=1}^{q} \mu(\alpha'_j) = \varepsilon,$$

is attained for $\mu(\alpha'_j) = \dfrac{\varepsilon}{q}$ $(1 \leq j \leq q)$ and is $\varepsilon \left[\lg q + \lg \dfrac{1}{\varepsilon} \right]$. Therefore, in our case

$$R < \lambda \left[\lg q + \lg \frac{1}{\lambda} \right].$$

But q is the number of sequences in the low probability group and is less than a^n, the number of all n-term sequences, (a is the number of letters in the alphabet A_0.) Therefore

$$R < \lambda n \lg a + \lambda \lg \frac{1}{\lambda} < \lambda n \lg a + 1.$$

We see that $R = o(n)$ as $n \to \infty$, and since $H_\beta(\alpha) = o(n)$, as we proved earlier, it follows from (16.3) that

(16.5)
$$H_\beta(\alpha, \alpha') = o(n) \quad (n \to \infty).$$

We now change our notation somewhat. By the space $\alpha(\alpha_1, \alpha_2, \cdots)$ we shall mean the set of all n-term sequences of letters from the alphabet A_0, whether from the high probability or low probability groups, so that the number of all α_i is a^n, where a is the number of letters in the alphabet A_0. As before, the space $\beta(\beta_1, \beta_2, \cdots)$ denotes the set of all n-term sequences of letters from the alphabet B. The product (α, β) of these two spaces has the distribution

$$\omega(\alpha_i, \beta_k) = \int_{\alpha_i} \lambda_\theta(\beta_k) \, d\mu(\theta) = \lambda_{\alpha_i}(\beta_k) \, \mu(\alpha_i),$$

and the distributions of the spaces α and β are given by the functions $\mu(\alpha_i)$ and

$$\eta(\beta_k) = \omega(A_0^I, \beta_k) = \sum_i \mu(\alpha_i)\,\lambda_{\alpha_i}(\beta_k),$$

respectively. The conditional entropy of the space α for a given β_k, averaged over β_k, which we denote by $H_\beta(\alpha)$ is obviously the quantity $H_\beta(\alpha, \alpha')$ which we have just estimated. Therefore, by (16.5) we have

(16.6) $\qquad\qquad H_\beta(\alpha) = o(n) \quad (n \to \infty)$.

The information transmission process which we are considering is the following. The output of the source $[A_0, \mu]$ is "cut up" into sequences of length n, and each such sequence α_i is transmitted through the channel $[A_0, \lambda_\theta, B]$, giving at the output a sequence of $n+m$ letters from the alphabet A. The last n letters of this sequence form the "received" sequences β_k. The output of our transmission process consists of a sequence of such sequences. Our problem is to estimate the rate of transmission. To do this, we consider a sequence of length $s = nt + r$ from the output of the source $[A_0, \mu]$, where t is any positive integer and $0 \leq r < n$. We denote such a sequence by X and the set (space) of all such sequences (for a given s) by $\{X\}$. Let the s-term sequence Y (of letters from the alphabet B) be received at the channel output, when the sequence X is transmitted through the channel $[A_0, \lambda_0, B]$, and let $\{Y\}$ denote the set (space) of all such sequences Y. We denote by $H_Y(X)$ the conditional entropy of the space $\{X\}$, averaged over Y.

Each sequence X of length $s = nt + r$ can be decomposed into t consecutive sequences $\alpha^{(1)}, \alpha^{(2)}, \cdots, \alpha^{(t)}$ of length n and a "residual" sequence α^* of length $r < n$. Clearly we can regard the space $\{X\}$ as the product of the $t+1$ spaces $\{\alpha^{(j)}\}$ $(1 \leq j \leq t)$ and $\{\alpha^*\}$, where each of the first t spaces has the structure of the space which we considered above. It is obvious that in general the $t+1$ spaces will be mutually dependent. Because of the basic property of the entropy of a product space, we have

$$H_{Y_0}(X) \leq \sum_{j=1}^{t} H_{Y_0}[\alpha^{(j)}] + H_{Y_0}(\alpha^*),$$

where Y_0 is any fixed sequence of Y. Thus, averaging over Y_0, we find

(16.7) $$H_Y(X) \leq \sum_{j=1}^{t} H_Y[\alpha^{(j)}] + H_Y(\alpha^*).$$

Just as we decomposed the sequence X into t sequences $\alpha^{(j)}$ and the residual sequence α^*, we can decompose the sequence Y into t sequences $\beta^{(j)}$ $(1 \leq j \leq t)$ of length n and a residual sequence β^* of length $r < n$. Then the space $\{Y\}$ will be the product of the $t+1$ spaces $\{\beta^{(j)}\}$ $(1 \leq j \leq t)$ and $\{\beta^*\}$. The sequence $\beta^{(j)}$ $(1 \leq j \leq t)$ is the sequence at the channel output corresponding to the sequence $\alpha^{(j)}$ at its input. Therefore the product space $\{\alpha^{(j)}, \beta^{(j)}\}$ $(1 \leq j \leq t)$ has the distribution $\omega(\alpha_i, \beta_k)$ considered above, and the space $\{\beta_k^{(j)}\}$ has the distribution $\eta(\beta_k)$. Let $B^{(j)}$ $(1 \leq j \leq t)$ denote the set of all the sequences $\beta^{(l)}$ $(1 \leq l \leq t)$ and β^* which make up Y, *with the exception of* $\beta^{(j)}$. Then in order to fix a specific sequence Y, we must fix $\beta^{(j)}$ and $B^{(j)}$. In other words, we can regard the space $\{Y\}$ as the product of the spaces $\{\beta^{(j)}\}$ and $B^{(j)}$. (Here j is any of the numbers $1, 2, \cdots t$.) Therefore, by Lemma 1.2, we find for any j $(1 \leq j \leq t)$

(16.8) $$H_Y[\alpha^{(j)}] = H_{\beta^{(j)} B^{(j)}}[\alpha^{(j)}] \leq H_{\beta^{(j)}}[\alpha^{(j)}] = H_\beta(\alpha).$$

On the other hand, the space $\{\alpha^*\}$ obviously contains a^r events, where a is the number of letters in the alphabet A_0. But by one of the fundamental properties of the entropy the entropy of a finite space does not exceed the logarithm of the number of events in the space (see [1], [5]). · Therefore, for any choice of the sequence Y_0

$$H_{Y_0}(\alpha^*) \leqq r \lg a < n \lg a$$

and, consequently, the averaged conditional entropy $H_Y(\alpha^*)$ satisfies

(16.9) $$H_Y(\alpha^*) < n \lg a.$$

Then by (16.8) and (16.9), the inequality (16.7) gives

$$H_Y(X) \leqq t\, H_\beta(\alpha) + n \lg a,$$

from which it follows by (16.6), that for arbitrarily small $\lambda > 0$, for sufficiently large n, and for any $t \geqq 1$

$$H_Y(X) < \lambda t n + n \lg a \leqq \lambda s + n \lg a.$$

Now we recall that in #10 we characterized the quantity $H_Y(X)$, the "residual entropy" of the sequence X after it has been transmitted through the channel, as the amount of information remaining in the sequence after transmission, i.e., lost during transmission. Since the amount of information contained in the sequence X prior to transmission is sH_0, the amount of information transmitted is $sH_0 - H_Y(X)$. But transmitting each sequence $\alpha^{(j)}$ (of length n) requires the passage of $n+m$ symbols through the channel, and just as many symbols are necessary for transmitting the sequence α^*. Therefore the total number of symbols passing through the channel during the transmission of the sequence X is $(t+1)(n+m)$. Thus, one symbol at the channel output carries on the average an amount of information

$$\frac{sH_0-H_Y(X)}{(t+1)(n+m)}\geqq\frac{sH_0-\lambda s-n\lg a}{n(t+1)\left(1+\dfrac{m}{n}\right)}\geqq\frac{sH_0-\lambda s-n\lg a}{(s+n)\left(1+\dfrac{m}{n}\right)}=\frac{H_0-\lambda-\dfrac{n\lg a}{s}}{\left(1+\dfrac{n}{s}\right)\left(1+\dfrac{m}{n}\right)}.$$

If we select n large enough so that $\dfrac{m}{n}<\varepsilon$ and then t large enough so that $\dfrac{n}{s}\leqq\dfrac{1}{t}<\varepsilon$, then the right side will be larger than

$$\frac{H_0-\lambda-\varepsilon\lg a}{(1+\varepsilon)^2}<H_0-2\lambda,$$

if ε sufficiently small. This very important result means that with the coding selected each letter received at the channel output brings on the average an amount of information as close as desired to that which one letter carries on the average at the source output. In other words, the transmission of information occurs at a rate arbitrarily close to that at which the information is emitted by the driving source. Of course, all this is only under the condition that $H_0<C$, and for coding of sufficiently long sequences. In this regard, we note that if n must be taken too large, then the practical value of the coding method described is nullified, since one would have to wait too long to decode (decipher) the text received at the channel output. Thus, from the practical point of view, it would be of considerable interest to investigate the relation between n and λ. Feinstein [4] obtained some interesting results in this direction, but we shall not go into them here. From the purely practical point of view, we must note again that in both the Feinstein and the Shannon methods the construction of a code with the required characteristics is not given; the existence of

such a code is proved, but no indication is given of how to actually find it.

The result which we have obtained is the second Shannon theorem, and can be stated as follows.

Theorem.

Under the conditions of the theorem of #15, there exists a code such that the rate of transmission is as close to H_0 as desired.

Conclusion

The proof given above, which is based on the ideas of Shannon, McMillan, and Feinstein, is certainly long and complicated. However, it rests entirely on a single central idea which, when correctly understood, makes very transparent all the different steps of the complicated demonstration. Therefore, we consider it expedient to stress again, in somewhat more detail, the basic idea which lies behind all our considerations.

The channel we are given is a noisy channel. This means that we cannot determine the sequences of symbols sent at the channel input from the sequences received at the channel output; because of noise, two different sequences at the channel input can give rise to the same sequence at the output. The situation is considerably improved if we know two groups B_1 and B_2 of n-term sequences at the channel output such that 1) B_1 and B_2 do not contain any sequence in common, and 2) with overwhelming probability, the first of the two sequences which might be sent is mapped into one of the sequences of the group B_1, and the second into one of the sequences of the group B_2. In this case, by receiving a sequence of group B_1 at the channel output, we can almost be assured that the message was the first of the two possible sequences, whereas if a sequence of the group B_2 is received at the output, then it is almost certain that the second sequence was the message. Thus, under the circumstances which we have described, these two transmitted sequences are *distinguishable*. Groups of three, four, and more distinguishable sequences (as yet we do not touch upon the question of the existence of such groups) can be determined at the channel input in exactly the same way. Suppose we were able to find a group consisting of a large number K of such distinguishable n-term sequences at the channel input. If we could limit ourselves to sending only sequences belonging to this group, then from the sequence received at the channel output, we would be able to determine almost without error the sequence transmitted.

Can we do this? Obviously, in order to do so, it is necessary that the number L of different n-term sequences from the output of the given source which it is required to transmit through the channel, should not exceed K; for under this condition (and only under this condition) will it be possible for us to code the whole group of L such sequences which might have to be transmitted into our "distinguishable" group of K sequences at the channel input. Thus, the inequality $L < K$ serves as a criterion of the possibility of transmitting almost without error, and our efforts must be directed towards making L as small as possible and K as large as possible. The first goal is attained by using McMillan's theorem (Ch. II). By neglecting the "low probability" group (with total probability as small as desired) and, consequently, restricting ourselves to transmitting sequences from the "high probability" group. we greatly reduce the number of these sequences, and make it approximately equal to 2^{nH_0}, where H_0 is the entropy of the given source. The second problem is solved using Feinstein's fundamental lemma (Ch. IV), which asserts the existence of distinguishable groups for which the number of terms is $K > 2^{n(C-\varepsilon)}$, where C is the (ergodic) capacity of the channel, and ε is a positive number as small as desired. If $H_0 < C$, then we see at once that we have $L < K$ for a suitable choice of the distinguishable groups, and our problem is solved.

This is the central idea of the proof. All the rest is merely technique, although this technique sometimes requires great ingenuity in overcoming difficulties which arise.

In all the formulations of the Shannon theorems which exist in the literature, these theorems are accompanied by the converse proposition: if $H_0 > C$, then coding with the required effect is impossible. All authors regard this statement as almost obvious and allot its proof only several lines. In the version of the proof which is given in this paper, I do not see the possibility of proving these converse propositions. The whole matter here is the definition of C, a definition which, in my opinion, is usually given rather carelessly. It is said that the capacity C of a given channel is the least upper bound of the rate of transmission over this channel of the output of all possible sources (the alphabet of which coincides with the input alphabet of the channel.) As far as I can see, here the words "all possible sources" must be replaced by the words "all possible ergodic sources". (Consequently, the capacity which I define is called "ergodic".) Without this addition, the proofs of both McMillan and Feinstein break down at their central point. But if C is understood to be the ergodic capacity of the given channel (as is done in this paper) then the converse propositions mentioned above are not only not obvious, but apparently require essentially new ideas for their proof. I consider it possible that this difficulty can be overcome by using known limitations on admissible coding systems.

References

1. C. E. Shannon, *The mathematical theory of communication*, Bell Syst, Techn. Journ., **27**, 379–423; 623–656 (1948).
2. S. Goldman, *Information Theory*, Prentice-Hall, New York, (1954).
3. B. McMillan, *The basic theorems of information theory*, Ann. Math. Statistics, **24**, 196–219 (1953).
4. A. Feinstein, *A new basic theorem of information theory*, Trans. I.R.E., PGIT, 2–22, September (1954); identical with Technical Report No. 282, June (1954), Research Lab. of Electronics, Mass. Inst. of Technology.
5. A. Ya. Khinchin, *The entropy concept in probability theory*, the first of the papers translated here.
6. Hardy, Littlewood, and Pólya, *Inequalities*, Cambridge University Press (1934).
7. J. L. Doob, *Stochastic Processes*, John Wiley, New York (1953.)
8. E. Hopf, *Ergodentheorie*, Springer, Berlin (1937); reprinted by Chelsea Publishing Co., New York, 1948.
9. N. Wiener, Duke Math. Journ, **15**, 1–18 (1948).

(Translated by R. A. Silverman and M. D. Friedman)

Catalogue of Dover
SCIENCE BOOKS

DIFFERENTIAL EQUATIONS
(ORDINARY AND PARTIAL DIFFERENTIAL)

INTRODUCTION TO THE DIFFERENTIAL EQUATIONS OF PHYSICS, L. Hopf. Especially valuable to engineer with no math beyond elementary calculus. Emphasizes intuitive rather than formal aspects of concepts. Partial contents: Law of causality, energy theorem, damped oscillations, coupling by friction, cylindrical and spherical coordinates, heat source, etc. 48 figures. 160pp. 5⅜ x 8.   S120 Paperbound **$1.25**

INTRODUCTION TO BESSEL FUNCTIONS, F. Bowman. Rigorous, provides all necessary material during development, includes practical applications. Bessel functions of zero order, of any real order, definite integrals, asymptotic expansion, circular membranes, Bessel's solution to Kepler's problem, much more. "Clear . . . useful not only to students of physics and engineering, but to mathematical students in general," Nature. 226 problems. Short tables of Bessel functions. 27 figures. x + 135pp. 5⅜ x 8.   S462 Paperbound **$1.35**

DIFFERENTIAL EQUATIONS, F. R. Moulton. Detailed, rigorous exposition of all non-elementary processes of solving ordinary differential equations. Chapters on practical problems; more advanced than problems usually given as illustrations. Includes analytic differential equations; variations of a parameter; integrals of differential equations; analytic implicit functions; problems of elliptic motion; sine-amplitude functions; deviation of formal bodies; Cauchy-Lipshitz process; linear differential equations with periodic coefficients; much more. Historical notes. 10 figures. 222 problems. xv + 395pp. 5⅜ x 8.   S451 Paperbound **$2.00**

PARTIAL DIFFERENTIAL EQUATIONS OF MATHEMATICAL PHYSICS, A. G. Webster. Valuable sections on elasticity, compression theory, potential theory, theory of sound, heat conduction, wave propagation, vibration theory. Contents include: deduction of differential equations, vibrations, normal functions, Fourier's series. Cauchy's method, boundary problems, method of Riemann-Volterra, spherical, cylindrical, ellipsoidal harmonics, applications, etc. 97 figures. vii + 440pp. 5⅜ x 8.   S263 Paperbound **$2.00**

ORDINARY DIFFERENTIAL EQUATIONS, E. L. Ince. A most compendious analysis in real and complex domains. Existence and nature of solutions, continuous transformation groups, solutions in an infinite form, definite integrals, algebraic theory. Sturmian theory, boundary problems, existence theorems, 1st order, higher order, etc. "Deserves highest praise, a notable addition to mathematical literature," Bulletin, Amer. Math. Soc. Historical appendix. 18 figures. viii + 558pp. 5⅜ x 8.   S349 Paperbound **$2.55**

ASYMPTOTIC EXPANSIONS, A. Erdélyi. Only modern work available in English; unabridged reproduction of monograph prepared for Office of Naval Research. Discusses various procedures for asymptotic evaluation of integrals containing a large parameter; solutions of ordinary linear differential equations. vi + 108pp. 5⅜ x 8.   S318 Paperbound **$1.35**

LECTURES ON CAUCHY'S PROBLEM, J. Hadamard. Based on lectures given at Columbia, Rome, discusses work of Riemann, Kirchhoff, Volterra, and author's own research on hyperbolic case in linear partial differential equations. Extends spherical cylindrical waves to apply to all (normal) hyperbolic equations. Partial contents: Cauchy's problem, fundamental formula, equations with odd number, with even number of independent variables; method of descent. 32 figures. iii + 316pp. 5⅜ x 8.   S105 Paperbound **$1.75**

NUMBER THEORY

INTRODUCTION TO THE THEORY OF NUMBERS, L. E. Dickson. Thorough, comprehensive, witn adequate coverage of classical literature. Not beyond beginners. Chapters on divisibility, congruences, quadratic residues and reciprocity, Diophantine equations, etc. Full treatment of binary quadratic forms without usual restriction to integral coefficients. Covers infinitude of primes, Fermat's theorem, Legendre's symbol, automorphs, Recent theorems of Thue, Siegal, much more. Much material not readily available elsewhere. 239 problems. 1 figure. viii + 183pp. 5⅜ x 8.   S342 Paperbound **$1.65**

ELEMENTS OF NUMBER THEORY, I. M. Vinogradov. Detailed 1st course for persons without advanced mathematics; 95% of this book can be understood by readers who have gone no farther than high school algebra. Partial contents: divisibility theory, important number theoretical functions, congruences, primitive roots and indices, etc. Solutions to problems, exercises. Tables of primes, indices, etc. Covers almost every essential formula in elementary number theory! "Welcome addition . . . reads smoothly," Bull. of the Amer. Math. Soc. 233 problems. 104 exercises. viii + 227pp. 5⅜ x 8.   S259 Paperbound **$1.60**

PROBABILITY THEORY AND INFORMATION THEORY

SELECTED PAPERS ON NOISE AND STOCHASTIC PROCESSES, edited by Prof. Nelson Wax, U. of Illinois. 6 basic papers for those whose work involves noise characteristics. Chandrasekhar, Uhlenback and Ornstein, Uhlenbeck and Ming, Rice, Doob. Included is Kac's Chauvenet-Prize winning "Random Walk." Extensive bibliography lists 200 articles, through 1953. 21 figures. 337pp. 6⅛ x 9¼.   S262 Paperbound **$2.35**

A PHILOSOPHICAL ESSAY ON PROBABILITIES, Marquis de Laplace. This famous essay explains without recourse to mathematics the principle of probability, and the application of probability to games of chance, natural philosophy, astronomy, many other fields. Translated from 6th French edition by F. W. Truscott, F. L. Emory. Intro. by E. T. Bell. 204pp. 5⅜ x 8.   S166 Paperbound **$1.25**

MATHEMATICAL FOUNDATIONS OF INFORMATION THEORY, A. I. Khinchin. For mathematicians, statisticians, physicists, cyberneticists, communications engineers, a complete, exact introduction to relatively new field. Entropy as a measure of a finite scheme, applications to coding theory, study of sources, channels and codes, detailed proofs of both Shannon theorems for any ergodic source and any stationary channel with finite memory, much more. "Presents for the first time rigorous proofs of certain fundamental theorems . . . quite complete . . . amazing expository ability," American Math. Monthly. vii + 120pp. 5⅜ x 8.   S434. Paperbound **$1.35**

VECTOR AND TENSOR ANALYSIS AND MATRIX THEORY

VECTOR AND TENSOR ANALYSIS, G. E. Hay. One of clearest introductions to increasingly important subject. Start with simple definitions, finish with sure mastery of oriented Cartesian vectors, Christoffel symbols, solenoidal tensors. Complete breakdown of plane, solid, analytical, differential geometry. Separate chapters on application. All fundamental formulae listed, demonstrated. 195 problems. 66 figures. viii + 193pp. 5⅜ x 8.   S109 Paperbound **$1.75**

APPLICATIONS OF TENSOR ANALYSIS, A. J. McConnell. Excellent text for applying tensor methods to such familiar subjects as dynamics, electricity, elasticity, hydrodynamics. Explains fundamental ideas and notation of tensor theory, geometrical treatment of tensor algebra, theory of differentiation of tensors, and a wealth of practical material. "The variety of fields treated and the presence of extremely numerous examples make this volume worth much more than its low price," Alluminio. Formerly titled "Applications of the Absolute Differential Calculus." 43 illustrations. 685 problems. xii + 381pp.   S373 Paperbound **$1.85**

VECTOR AND TENSOR ANALYSIS, A. P. Wills. Covers entire field, from dyads to non-Euclidean manifolds (especially detailed), absolute differentiation, the Riemann-Christoffel and Ricci-Einstein tensors, calculation of Gaussian curvature of a surface. Illustrations from electrical engineering, relativity theory, astro-physics, quantum mechanics. Presupposes only working knowledge of calculus. Intended for physicists, engineers, mathematicians. 44 diagrams. 114 problems. xxxii + 285pp. 5⅜ x 8.   S454 Paperbound **$1.75**

DOVER SCIENCE BOOKS

PHYSICS, ENGINEERING

MECHANICS, DYNAMICS, THERMODYNAMICS, ELASTICITY

MATHEMATICAL ANALYSIS OF ELECTRICAL AND OPTICAL WAVE-MOTION, H. Bateman. By one of century's most distinguished mathematical physicists, a practical introduction to developments of Maxwell's electromagnetic theory which directly concern the solution of partial differential equation of wave motion. Methods of solving wave-equation, polar-cylindrical coordinates, diffraction, transformation of coordinates, homogeneous solutions, electromagnetic fields with moving singularities, etc. 168pp. 5⅜ x 8.　　　　　　　　S14 Paperbound **$1.60**

THERMODYNAMICS, Enrico Fermi. Unabridged reproduction of 1937 edition. Remarkable for clarity, organization; requires no knowledge of advanced math beyond calculus, only familiarity with fundamentals of thermometry, calorimetry. Partial Contents: Thermodynamic systems, 1st and 2nd laws, potentials; Entropy, phase rule; Reversible electric cells; Gaseous reactions: Van't Hoff reaction box, principle of LeChatelier; Thermodynamics of dilute solutions: osmotic, vapor pressures; boiling, freezing point; Entropy constant. 25 problems. 24 illustrations. x + 160pp. 5⅜ x 8.　　　　　　　　S361 Paperbound **$1.75**

FOUNDATIONS OF POTENTIAL THEORY, O. D. Kellogg. Based on courses given at Harvard, suitable for both advanced and beginning mathematicians, Proofs rigorous, much material here not generally available elsewhere. Partial contents: gravity, fields of force, divergence theorem, properties of Newtonian potentials at points of free space, potentials as solutions of LaPlace's equation, harmonic functions, electrostatics, electric images, logarithmic potential, etc. ix + 384pp. 5⅜ x 8.　　　　　　　　S144 Paperbound **$1.98**

DIALOGUES CONCERNING TWO NEW SCIENCES, Galileo Galilei. Classic of experimental science, mechanics, engineering, as enjoyable as it is important. Characterized by author as "superior to everything else of mine." Offers a lively exposition of dynamics, elasticity, sound, ballistics, strength of materials, scientific method. Translated by H. Grew, A. de Salvio. 126 diagrams. xxi + 288pp. 5⅜ x 8.　　　　　　　　S99 Paperbound **$1.65**

THEORETICAL MECHANICS; AN INTRODUCTION TO MATHEMATICAL PHYSICS, J. S. Ames, F. D. Murnaghan. A mathematically rigorous development for advanced students, with constant practical applications. Used in hundreds of advanced courses. Unusually thorough coverage of gyroscopic baryscopic material, detailed analyses of Corilis acceleration, applications of Lagrange's equations, motion of double pendulum, Hamilton-Jacobi partial differential equations, group velocity, dispersion, etc. Special relativity included. 159 problems. 44 figures. ix + 462pp. 5⅜ x 8.　　　　　　　　S461 Paperbound **$2.00**

STATICS AND THE DYNAMICS OF A PARTICLE, W. D. MacMillan. This is Part One of "Theoretical Mechanics." For over 3 decades a self-contained, extremely comprehensive advanced undergraduate text in mathematical physics, physics, astronomy, deeper foundations of engineering. Early sections require only a knowledge of geometry; later, a working knowledge of calculus. Hundreds of basic problems including projectiles to moon, harmonic motion, ballistics, transmission of power, stress and strain, elasticity, astronomical problems. 340 practice problems, many fully worked out examples. 200 figures. xvii + 430pp. 5⅜ x 8.　　　　　　　　S467 Paperbound **$2.00**

THE THEORY OF THE POTENTIAL, W. D. MacMillan. This is Part Two of "Theoretical Mechanics." Comprehensive, well-balanced presentation, serving both as introduction and reference with regard to specific problems, for physicists and mathematicians. Assumes no prior knowledge of integral relations, all math is developed as needed. Includes: Attraction of Finite Bodies; Newtonian Potential Function; Vector Fields, Green and Gauss Theorems; Two-layer Surfaces; Spherical Harmonics; etc. "The great number of particular cases . . . should make the book valuable to geo-physicists and others actively engaged in practical applications of the potential theory," Review of Scientific Instruments. xii + 469pp. 5⅜ x 8.　　　　　　　　S486 Paperbound **$2.25**

DYNAMICS OF A SYSTEM OF RIGID BODIES (Advanced Section), E. J. Routh. Revised 6th edition of a classic reference aid. Partial contents: moving axes, relative motion, oscillations about equilibrium, motion. Motion of a body under no forces, any forces. Nature of motion given by linear equations and conditions of stability. Free, forced vibrations, constants of integration, calculus of finite differences, variations, procession and mutation, motion of the moon, motion of string, chain, membranes. 64 figures. 498pp. 5⅜ x 8.　　　　　　　　S229 Paperbound **$2.35**

THE DYNAMICS OF PARTICLES AND OF RIGID, ELASTIC, AND FLUID BODIES: BEING LECTURES ON MATHEMATICAL PHYSICS, A. G. Webster. Reissuing of classic fills need for comprehensive work on dynamics. Covers wide range in unusually great depth, applying ordinary, partial differential equations. Partial contents: laws of motion, methods applicable to systems of all sorts; oscillation, resonance, cyclic systems; dynamics of rigid bodies; potential theory; stress and strain; gyrostatics; wave, vortex motion; kinematics of a point; Lagrange's equations; Hamilton's principle; vectors; deformable bodies; much more not easily found together in one volume. Unabridged reprinting of 2nd edition. 20 pages on differential equations, higher analysis. 203 illustrations. xi + 588pp. 5⅜ x 8. S522 Paperbound **$2.35**

PRINCIPLES OF MECHANICS, Heinrich Hertz. A classic of great interest in logic of science. Last work by great 19th century physicist, created new system of mechanics based upon space, time, mass; returns to axiomatic analysis, understanding of formal, structural aspects of science, taking into account logic, observation, a priori elements. Of great historical importance to Poincaré, Carnap, Einstein, Milne. 20 page introduction by R. S. Cohen, Wesleyan U., analyzes implications of Hertz's thought and logic of science. 13 page introduction by Helmholtz. xlii + 274pp. 5⅜ x 8. S316 Clothbound **$3.50**
S317 Paperbound **$1.75**

MATHEMATICAL FOUNDATIONS OF STATISTICAL MECHANICS, A. I. Khinchin. A thoroughly up-to-date introduction, offering a precise and mathematically rigorous formulation of the problems of statistical mechanics. Provides analytical tools to replace many commonly used cumbersome concepts and devices. Partial contents: Geometry, kinematics of phase space; ergodic problem; theory of probability; central limit theorem; ideal monatomic gas; foundation of thermodynamics; dispersion, distribution of sum functions; etc. "Excellent introduction . . . clear, concise, rigorous," Quarterly of Applied Mathematics. viii + 179pp. 5⅜ x 8. S146 Clothbound **$2.95**
S147 Paperbound **$1.35**

MECHANICS OF THE GYROSCOPE, THE DYNAMICS OF ROTATION, R. F. Deimel, Prof. of Mechanical Engineering, Stevens Inst. of Tech. Elementary, general treatment of dynamics of rotation, with special application of gyroscopic phenomena. No knowledge of vectors needed. Velocity of a moving curve, acceleration to a point, general equations of motion, gyroscopic horizon, free gyro, motion of discs, the damped gyro, 103 similar topics. Exercises. 75 figures. 208pp. 5⅜ x 8. S66 Paperbound **$1.65**

MECHANICS VIA THE CALCULUS, P. W. Norris, W. S. Legge. Wide coverage, from linear motion to vector analysis; equations determining motion, linear methods, compounding of simple harmonic motions, Newton's laws of motion, Hooke's law, the simple pendulum, motion of a particle in 1 plane, centers of gravity, virtual work, friction, kinetic energy of rotating bodies, equilibrium of strings, hydrostatics, sheering stresses, elasticity, etc. Many worked-out examples. 550 problems. 3rd revised edition. xii + 367pp. S207 Clothbound **$3.95**

A TREATISE ON THE MATHEMATICAL THEORY OF ELASTICITY, A. E. H. Love. An indispensable reference work for engineers, mathematicians, physicists, the most complete, authoritative treatment of classical elasticity in one volume. Proceeds from elementary notions of extension to types of strain, cubical dilatation, general theory of strains. Covers relation between mathematical theory of elasticity and technical mechanics; equilibrium of isotropic elastic solids and aelotropic solid bodies; nature of force transmission, Volterra's theory of dislocations; theory of elastic spheres in relation to tidal, rotational, gravitational effects on earth; general theory of bending; deformation of curved plates; buckling effects; much more. "The standard treatise on elasticity," American Math. Monthly. 4th revised edition. 76 figures. xviii + 643pp. 6⅛ x 9¼. S174 Paperbound **$2.95**

NUCLEAR PHYSICS, QUANTUM THEORY, RELATIVITY

MESON PHYSICS, R. E. Marshak. Presents basic theory, and results of experiments with emphasis on theoretical significance. Phenomena involving mesons as virtual transitions avoided, eliminating some of least satisfactory predictions of meson theory. Includes production study of π mesons at nonrelativistic nucleon energies contracts between π and u mesons, phenomena associated with nuclear interaction of π mesons, etc. Presents early evidence for new classes of particles, indicates theoretical difficulties created by discovery of heavy mesons and hyperons. viii + 378pp. 5⅜ x 8. S500 Paperbound **$1.95**

THE FUNDAMENTAL PRINCIPLES OF QUANTUM MECHANICS, WITH ELEMENTARY APPLICATIONS, E. C. Kemble. Inductive presentation, for graduate student, specialists in other branches of physics. Apparatus necessary beyond differential equations and advanced calculus developed as needed. Though general exposition of principles, hundreds of individual problems fully treated. "Excellent book . . . of great value to every student . . . rigorous and detailed mathematical discussion . .. has succeeded in keeping his presentation clear and understandable," Dr. Linus Pauling, J. of American Chemical Society. Appendices: calculus of variations, math. notes, etc. 611pp. 5⅝ x 8⅜. T472 Paperbound **$2.95**

WAVE PROPAGATION IN PERIODIC STRUCTURES, L. Brillouin. General method, application to different problems: pure physics—scattering of X-rays in crystals, thermal vibration in crystal lattices, electronic motion in metals; problems in electrical engineering. Partial contents: elastic waves along 1-dimensional lattices of point masses. Propagation of waves along 1-dimensional lattices. Energy flow. 2, 3 dimensional lattices. Mathieu's equation. Matrices and propagation of waves along an electric line. Continuous electric lines. 131 illustrations. xii + 253pp. 5⅜ x 8. S34 Paperbound **$1.85**

DOVER SCIENCE BOOKS

THEORY OF ELECTRONS AND ITS APPLICATION TO THE PHENOMENA OF LIGHT AND RADIANT HEAT, H. Lorentz. Lectures delivered at Columbia Univ., by Nobel laureate. Unabridged, form historical coverage of theory of free electrons, motion, absorption of heat, Zeeman effect, optical phenomena in moving bodies, etc. 109 pages notes explain more advanced sections. 9 figures. 352pp. 5⅜ x 8. S173 Paperbound **$1.85**

SELECTED PAPERS ON QUANTUM ELECTRODYNAMICS, edited by J. Schwinger. Facsimiles of papers which established quantum electrodynamics; beginning to present position as part of larger theory. First book publication in any language of collected papers of Bethe, Bloch, Dirac, Dyson, Fermi, Feynman, Heisenberg, Kusch, Lamb, Oppenheimer, Pauli, Schwinger, Tomonoga, Weisskopf, Wigner, etc. 34 papers: 29 in English, 1 in French, 3 in German, 1 in Italian. Historical commentary by editor. xvii + 423pp. 6⅛ x 9¼. S444 Paperbound **$2.45**

FOUNDATIONS OF NUCLEAR PHYSICS, edited by R. T. Beyer. 13 of the most important papers on nuclear physics reproduced in facsimile in the original languages; the papers most often cited in footnotes, bibliographies. Anderson, Curie, Joliot, Chadwick, Fermi, Lawrence, Cockroft, Hahn, Yukawa. Unparalleled bibliography: 122 double columned pages, over 4,000 articles, books, classified. 57 figures. 288pp. 6⅛ x 9¼. S19 Paperbound **$1.75**

THE THEORY OF GROUPS AND QUANTUM MECHANICS, H. Weyl. Schroedinger's wave equation, de Broglie's waves of a particle, Jordon-Hoelder theorem, Lie's continuous groups of transformations, Pauli exclusion principle, quantization of Mawell-Dirac field equations, etc. Unitary geometry, quantum theory, groups, application of groups to quantum mechanics, symmetry permutation group, algebra of symmetric transformations, etc. 2nd revised edition. xxii + 422pp. 5⅜ x 8. S268 Clothbound **$4.50**
S269 Paperbound **$1.95**

PHYSICAL PRINCIPLES OF THE QUANTUM THEORY, Werner Heisenberg. Nobel laureate discusses quantum theory; his own work, Compton, Schroedinger, Wilson, Einstein, many others. For physicists, chemists, not specialists in quantum theory. Only elementary formulae considered in text; mathematical appendix for specialists. Profound without sacrificing clarity. Translated by C. Eckart, F. Hoyt. 18 figures. 192pp. 5⅜ x 8. S113 Paperbound **$1.25**

INVESTIGATIONS ON THE THEORY OF THE BROWNIAN MOVEMENT, Albert Einstein. Reprints from rare European journals, translated into English. 5 basic papers, including Elementary Theory of the Brownian Movement, written at request of Lorentz to provide a simple explanation. Translated by A. D. Cowper. Annotated, edited by R. Fürth. 33pp. of notes elucidate, give history of previous investigations. 62 footnotes. 124pp. 5⅜ x 8. S304 Paperbound **$1.25**

THE PRINCIPLE OF RELATIVITY, E. Einstein, H. Lorentz, M. Minkowski, H. Weyl. The 11 basic papers that founded the general and special theories of relativity, translated into English. 2 papers by Lorentz on the Michelson experiment, electromagnetic phenomena. Minkowski's "Space and Time," and Weyl's "Gravitation and Electricity." 7 epoch-making papers by Einstein: "Electromagnetics of Moving Bodies," "Influence of Gravitation in Propagation of Light," "Cosmological Considerations," "General Theory," 3 others. 7 diagrams. Special notes by A. Sommerfeld. 224pp. 5⅜ x 8. S93 Paperbound **$1.75**

STATISTICS

ELEMENTARY STATISTICS, WITH APPLICATIONS IN MEDICINE AND THE BIOLOGICAL SCIENCES, F. E. Croxton. Based primarily on biological sciences, but can be used by anyone desiring introduction to statistics. Assumes no prior acquaintance, requires only modest knowledge of math. All basic formulas carefully explained, illustrated; all necessary reference tables included. From basic terms and concepts, proceeds to frequency distribution, linear, non-linear, multiple correlation, etc. Contains concrete examples from medicine, biology. 101 charts. 57 tables. 14 appendices. Iv + 376pp. 5⅜ x 8. S506 Paperbound **$1.95**

ANALYSIS AND DESIGN OF EXPERIMENTS, H. B. Mann. Offers method for grasping analysis of variance, variance design quickly. Partial contents: Chi-square distribution, analysis of variance distribution, matrices, quadratic forms, likelihood ration tests, test of linear hypotheses, power of analysis, Galois fields, non-orthogonal data, interblock estimates, etc. 15pp. of useful tables. x + 195pp. 5 x 7⅜. S180 Paperbound **$1.45**

FREQUENCY CURVES AND CORRELATION, W. P. Elderton. 4th revised edition of standard work on classical statistics. Practical, one of few books constantly referred to for clear presentation of basic material. Partial contents: Frequency Distributions; Pearsons Frequency Curves; Theoretical Distributions; Standard Errors; Correlation Ratio—Contingency; Corrections for Moments, Beta, Gamma Functions; etc. Key to terms, symbols. 25 examples. 40 tables. 16 figures. xi + 272pp. 5½ x 8½. Clothbound **$1.49**

HYDRODYNAMICS, ETC.

HYDRODYNAMICS, Horace Lamb. Standard reference work on dynamics of liquids and gases. Fundamental theorems, equations, methods, solutions, background for classical hydrodynamics. Chapters: Equations of Motion, Integration of Equations in Special Gases, Vortex Motion, Tidal Waves, Rotating Masses of Liquids, etc. Excellently planned, arranged, Clear, lucid presentation. 6th enlarged, revised edition. Over 900 footnotes, mostly bibliographical. 119 figures. xv + 738pp. 6⅛ x 9¼.   S256 Paperbound **$2.95**

HYDRODYNAMICS, A STUDY OF LOGIC, FACT, AND SIMILITUDE, Garrett Birkhoff. A stimulating application of pure mathematics to an applied problem. Emphasis is on correlation of theory and deduction with experiment. Examines recently discovered paradoxes, theory of modelling and dimensional analysis, paradox and error in flows and free boundary theory. Classical theory of virtual mass derived from homogenous spaces; group theory applied to fluid mechanics. 20 figures, 3 plates. xiii + 186pp. 5⅜ x 8.   S22 Paperbound **$1.85**

HYDRODYNAMICS, H. Dryden, F. Murhaghan, H. Bateman. Published by National Research Council, 1932. Complete coverage of classical hydrodynamics, encyclopedic in quality. Partial contents: physics of fluids, motion, turbulent flow, compressible fluids, motion in 1, 2, 3 dimensions; laminar motion, resistance of motion through viscous fluid, eddy viscosity, discharge of gases, flow past obstacles, etc. Over 2900-item bibliography. 23 figures. 634pp. 5⅜ x 8.   S303 Paperbound **$2.75**

ACOUSTICS AND OPTICS

PRINCIPLES OF PHYSICAL OPTICS, Ernst Mach. Classical examination of propagation of light, color, polarization, etc. Historical, philosophical treatment unequalled for breadth and readability. Contents: Rectilinear propagation, reflection, refraction, dioptrics, composition of light, periodicity, theory of interference, polarization, mathematical representation of properties, etc. 279 illustrations. 10 portraits. 324pp. 5⅜ x 8.   S170 Paperbound **$1.75**

THE THEORY OF SOUND, Lord Rayleigh. Written by Nobel laureate, classical methods here will cover most vibrating systems likely to be encountered in practice. Complete coverage of experimental, mathematical aspects. Partial contents: Harmonic motions, lateral vibrations of bars, curved plates or shells, applications of Laplace's functions to acoustical problems, fluid friction, etc. First low-priced edition of this great reference-study work. Historical introduction by R. B. Lindsay. 1040pp. 97 figures. 5⅜ x 8.
S292, S293, Two volume set, paperbound **$4.00**

THEORY OF VIBRATIONS, N. W. McLachlan. Based on exceptionally successful graduate course, Brown University. Discusses linear systems having 1 degree of freedom, forced vibrations of simple linear systems, vibration of flexible strings, transverse vibrations of bars and tubes, of circular plate, sound waves of finite amplitude, etc. 99 diagrams. 160pp. 5⅜ x 8.   S190 Paperbound **$1.35**

APPLIED OPTICS AND OPTICAL DESIGN, A. E. Conrady. Thorough systematic presentation of physical and mathematical aspects, limited mostly to "real optics." Stresses practical problem of maximum aberration permissible without affecting performance. Ordinary ray tracing methods; complete theory ray tracing methods, primary aberrations; enough higher aberration to design telescopes, low powered microscopes, photographic equipment. Covers fundamental equations, extra-axial image points, transverse chromatic aberration, angular magnification, similar topics. Tables of functions of N. Over 150 diagrams. x + 518pp. 5⅜ x 8⅝.   S366 Paperbound **$2.98**

RAYLEIGH'S PRINCIPLE AND ITS APPLICATIONS TO ENGINEERING, G. Temple, W. Bickley. Rayleigh's principle developed to provide upper, lower estimates of true value of fundamental period of vibrating system, or condition of stability of elastic system. Examples, rigorous proofs. Partial contents: Energy method of discussing vibrations, stability. Perturbation theory, whirling of uniform shafts. Proof, accuracy, successive approximations, applications of Rayleigh's theory. Numerical, graphical methods. Ritz's method. 22 figures. ix + 156pp. 5⅜ x 8.   S307 Paperbound **$1.50**

OPTICKS, Sir Isaac Newton. In its discussion of light, reflection, color, refraction, theories of wave and corpuscular theories of light, this work is packed with scores of insights and discoveries. In its precise and practical discussions of construction of optical apparatus, contemporary understanding of phenomena, it is truly fascinating to modern scientists. Foreword by Albert Einstein. Preface by I. B. Cohen, Harvard. 7 pages of portraits, facsimile pages, letters, etc. cxvi + 414pp. 5⅜ x 8.   S205 Paperbound **$2.00**

DOVER SCIENCE BOOKS

ON THE SENSATIONS OF TONE, Hermann Helmholtz. Using acoustical physics, physiology, experiment, history of music, covers entire gamut of musical tone: relation of music science to acoustics, physical vs. physiological acoustics, vibration, resonance, tonality, progression of parts, etc. 33 appendixes on various aspects of sound, physics, acoustics, music, etc. Translated by A. J. Ellis. New introduction by H. Margenau, Yale. 68 figures. 43 musical passages analyzed. Over 100 tables. xix + 576pp. 6⅛ x 9¼.

S114 Clothbound **$4.95**

ELECTROMAGNETICS, ENGINEERING, TECHNOLOGY

INTRODUCTION TO RELAXATION METHODS, F. S. Shaw. Describes almost all manipulative resources of value in solution of differential equations. Treatment is mathematical rather than physical. Extends general computational process to include almost all branches of applied math and physics. Approximate numerical methods are demonstrated, although high accuracy is obtainable without undue expenditure of time. 48pp. of tables for computing irregular star first and second derivatives, irregular star coefficients for second order equations, for fourth order equations. "Useful. . . . exposition is clear, simple . . . no previous acquaintance with numerical methods is assumed," Science Progress. 253 diagrams. 72 tables. 400pp. 5⅜ x 8.

S244 Paperbound **$2.45**

THE ELECTROMAGNETIC FIELD, M. Mason, W. Weaver. Used constantly by graduate engineers. Vector methods exclusively; detailed treatment of electrostatics, expansion methods, with tables converting any quantity into absolute electromagnetic, absolute electrostatic, practical units. Discrete charges, ponderable bodies. Maxwell field equations, etc. 416pp. 5⅜ x 8.

S185 Paperbound **$2.00**

ELASTICITY, PLASTICITY AND STRUCTURE OF MATTER, R. Houwink. Standard treatise on rheological aspects of different technically important solids: crystals, resins, textiles, rubber, clay, etc. Investigates general laws for deformations; determines divergences. Covers general physical and mathematical aspects of plasticity, elasticity, viscosity. Detailed examination of deformations, internal structure of matter in relation to elastic, plastic behaviour, formation of solid matter from a fluid, etc. Treats glass, asphalt, balata, proteins, baker's dough, others. 2nd revised, enlarged edition. Extensive revised bibliography in over 500 footnotes. 214 figures. xvii + 368pp. 6 x 9¼.

S385 Paperbound **$2.45**

DESIGN AND USE OF INSTRUMENTS AND ACCURATE MECHANISM, T. N. Whitehead. For the instrument designer, engineer; how to combine necessary mathematical abstractions with independent observations of actual facts. Partial contents: instruments and their parts, theory of errors, systematic errors, probability, short period errors, erratic errors, design precision, kinematic, semikinematic design, stiffness, planning of an instrument, human factor, etc. 85 photos, diagrams. xii + 288pp. 5⅜ x 8.

S270 Paperbound **$1.95**

APPLIED HYDRO- AND AEROMECHANICS, L. Prandtl, O. G. Tietjens. Presents, for most part, methods valuable to engineers. Flow in pipes, boundary layers, airfoil theory, entry conditions, turbulent flow, boundary layer, determining drag from pressure and velocity, etc. "Will be welcomed by all students of aerodynamics," Nature. Unabridged, unaltered. An Engineering Society Monograph, 1934. Index. 226 figures. 28 photographic plates illustrating flow patterns. xvi + 311pp. 5⅜ x 8.

S375 Paperbound **$1.85**

FUNDAMENTALS OF HYDRO- AND AEROMECHANICS, L. Prandtl, O. G. Tietjens. Standard work, based on Prandtl's lectures at Goettingen. Wherever possible hydrodynamics theory is referred to practical considerations in hydraulics, unifying theory and experience. Presentation extremely clear. Though primarily physical, proofs are rigorous and use vector analysis to a great extent. An Engineering Society Monograph, 1934. "Still recommended as an excellent introduction to this area," Physikalische Blätter. 186 figures. xvi + 270pp. 5⅜ x 8.

S374 Paperbound **$1.85**

GASEOUS CONDUCTORS: THEORY AND ENGINEERING APPLICATIONS, J. D. Cobine. Indispensable text, reference, to gaseous conduction phenomena, with engineering viewpoint prevailing throughout. Studies kinetic theory of gases, ionization, emission phenomena; gas breakdown, spark characteristics, glow, discharges; engineering applications in circuit interrupters, rectifiers, etc. Detailed treatment of high pressure arcs (Suits); low pressure arcs (Langmuir, Tonks). Much more. "Well organized, clear, straightforward," Tonks, Review of Scientific Instruments. 83 practice problems. Over 600 figures. 58 tables. xx + 606pp. 5⅜ x 8.

S442 Paperbound **$2.75**

PHOTOELASTICITY: PRINCIPLES AND METHODS, H. T. Jessop, F. C. Harris. For engineer, specific problems of stress analysis. Latest time-saving methods of checking calculations in 2-dimensional design problems, new techniques for stresses in 3 dimensions, lucid description of optical systems used in practical photoelectricity. Useful suggestions, hints based on on-the-job experience included. Partial contents: strain, stress-strain relations, circular disc under thrust along diameter, rectangular block with square hold under vertical thrust, simply supported rectangular beam under central concentrated load, etc. Theory held to minimum, no advanced mathematical training needed. 164 illustrations. viii + 184pp. 6⅛ x 9¼.

S137 Clothbound **$3.75**

7

MICROWAVE TRANSMISSION DESIGN DATA, T. Moreno. Originally classified, now rewritten, enlarged (14 new chapters) under auspices of Sperry Corp. Of immediate value or reference use to radio engineers, systems designers, applied physicists, etc. Ordinary transmission line theory; attenuation; parameters of coaxial lines; flexible cables; tuneable wave guide impedance transformers; effects of temperature, humidity; much more. "Packed with information . . . theoretical discussions are directly related to practical questions," U. of Royal Naval Scientific Service. Tables of dielectrics, flexible cable, etc. ix + 248pp. 5⅜ x 8.
S549 Paperbound **$1.50**

THE THEORY OF THE PROPERTIES OF METALS AND ALLOYS, H. F. Mott, H. Jones. Quantum methods develop mathematical models showing interrelationship of fundamental chemical phenomena wtih crystal structure, electrical, optical properties, etc. Examines electron motion in applied field, cohesion, heat capacity, refraction, noble metals, transition and di-valent metals, etc. "Exposition is as clear . . . mathematical treatment as simple and reliable as we have become used to expect of . . . Prof. Mott," Nature. 138 figures. xiii + 320pp. 5⅜ x 8.
S456 Paperbound **$1.85**

THE MEASUREMENT OF POWER SPECTRA FROM THE POINT OF VIEW OF COMMUNICATIONS ENGINEERING, R. B. Blackman, J. W. Tukey. Pathfinding work reprinted from "Bell System Technical Journal." Various ways of getting practically useful answers in power spectra measurement, using results from both transmission and statistical estimation theory. Treats: Autocovariance, Functions and Power Spectra, Distortion, Heterodyne Filtering, Smoothing, Decimation Procedures, Transversal Filtering, much more. Appendix reviews fundamental Fourier techniques. Index of notation. Glossary of terms. 24 figures. 12 tables. 192pp. 5⅝ x 8⅝.
S507 Paperbound **$1.85**

TREATISE ON ELECTRICITY AND MAGNETISM, James Clerk Maxwell. For more than 80 years a seemingly inexhaustible source of leads for physicists, mathematicians, engineers. Total of 1082pp. on such topics as Measurement of Quantities, Electrostatics, Elementary Mathematical Theory of Electricity, Electrical Work and Energy in a System of Conductors, General Theorems, Theory of Electrical Images, Electrolysis, Conduction, Polarization, Dielectrics, Resistance, much more. "The greatest mathematical physicist since Newton," Sir James Jeans. 3rd edition. 107 figures, 21 plates. 1082pp. 5⅜ x 8.
S186 Clothbound **$4.95**

CHEMISTRY AND PHYSICAL CHEMISTRY

THE PHASE RULE AND ITS APPLICATIONS, Alexander Findlay. Covers chemical phenomena of 1 to 4 multiple component systems, the "standard work on the subject" (Nature). Completely revised, brought up to date by A. N. Campbell, N. O. Smith. New material on binary, tertiary liquid equilibria, solid solutions in ternary systems, quinary systems of salts, water, etc. Completely revised to triangular coordinates in ternary systems, clarified graphic representation, solid models, etc. 9th revised edition. 236 figures. 505 footnotes, mostly bibliographic. xii + 449pp. 5⅜ x 8.
S92 Paperbound **$2.45**

DYNAMICAL THEORY OF GASES, James Jeans. Divided into mathematical, physical chapters for convenience of those not expert in mathematics. Discusses mathematical theory of gas in steady state, thermodynamics, Bolzmann, Maxwell, kinetic theory, quantum theory, exponentials, etc. "One of the classics of scientific writing . . . as lucid and comprehensive an exposition of the kinetic theory as has ever been written," J. of Institute of Engineers. 4th enlarged edition, with new material on quantum theory, quantum dynamics, etc. 28 figures. 444pp. 6⅛ x 9¼.
S136 Paperbound **$2.45**

POLAR MOLECULES, Pieter Debye. Nobel laureate offers complete guide to fundamental electrostatic field relations, polarizability, molecular structure. Partial contents: electric intensity, displacement, force, polarization by orientation, molar polarization, molar refraction, halogen-hydrides, polar liquids, ionic saturation, dielectric constant, etc. Special chapter considers quantum theory. "Clear and concise . . . coordination of experimental results with theory will be readily appreciated," Electronics Industries. 172pp. 5⅜ x 8.
S63 Clothbound **$3.50**
S64 Paperbound **$1.50**

ATOMIC SPECTRA AND ATOMIC STRUCTURE, G. Herzberg. Excellent general survey for chemists, physicists specializing in other fields. Partial contents: simplest line spectra, elements of atomic theory; multiple structure of line spectra, electron spin; building-up principle, periodic system of elements; finer details of atomic spectra; hyperfine structure of spectral lines; some experimental results and applications. 80 figures. 20 tables. xiii + 257pp. 5⅜ x 8.
S115 Paperbound **$1.95**

TREATISE ON THERMODYNAMICS, Max Planck. Classic based on his original papers. Brilliant concepts of Nobel laureate make no assumptions regarding nature of heat, rejects earlier approaches of Helmholtz, Maxwell, to offer uniform point of view for entire field. Seminal work by founder of quantum theory, deducing new physical, chemical laws. A standard text, an excellent introduction to field for students with knowledge of elementary chemistry, physics, calculus. 3rd English edition. xvi + 297pp. 5⅜ x 8.
S219 Paperbound **$1.75**

KINETIC THEORY OF LIQUIDS, J. Frenkel. Regards kinetic theory of liquids as generalization, extension of theory of solid bodies, covers all types of arrangements of solids; thermal displacements of atoms; interstitial atoms, ions; orientational, rotational motion of molecules; transition between states of matter. Mathematical theory developed close to physical subject matter. "Discussed in a simple yet deeply penetrating fashion . . . will serve as seeds for a great many basic and applied developments in chemistry," J. of the Amer. Chemical Soc. 216 bibliographical footnotes. 55 figures. xi + 485pp. 5⅜ x 8.
S94 Clothbound **$3.95**
S95 Paperbound **$2.45**

ASTRONOMY

OUT OF THE SKY, H. H. Nininger. Non-technical, comprehensive introduction to "meteoritics" —science concerned with arrival of matter from outer space. By one of world's experts on meteorites, this book defines meteors and meteorites; studies fireball clusters and processions, meteorite composition, size, distribution, showers, explosions, origins, much more. viii + 336pp. 5⅜ x 8.
T519 Paperbound **$1.85**

AN INTRODUCTION TO THE STUDY OF STELLAR STRUCTURE, S. Chandrasekhar. Outstanding treatise on stellar dynamics by one of greatest astro-physicists. Examines relationship between loss of energy, mass, and radius of stars in steady state. Discusses thermodynamic laws from Caratheodory's axiomatic standpoint; adiabatic, polytropic laws; work of Ritter, Emden, Kelvin, etc.; Stroemgren envelopes as starter for theory of gaseous stars; Gibbs statistical mechanics (quantum); degenerate stellar configuration, theory of white dwarfs; etc. "Highest level of scientific merit," Bulletin. Amer. Math. Soc. 33 figures. 509pp. 5⅜ x 8.
S413 Paperbound **$2.75**

LES MÉTHODES NOVELLES DE LA MÉCANIQUE CÉLESTE, H. Poincaré. Complete French text of one of Poincaré's most important works. Revolutionized celestial mechanics: first use of integral invariants, first major application of linear differential equations, study of periodic orbits, lunar motion and Jupiter's satellites, three body problem, and many other important topics. "Started a new era . . . so extremely modern that even today few have mastered his weapons," E. T. Bell. 3 volumes. Total 1282pp. 6⅛ x 9¼.
Vol. 1 S401 Paperbound **$2.75**
Vol. 2 S402 Paperbound **$2.75**
Vol. 3 S403 Paperbound **$2.75**
The set **$7.50**

THE REALM OF THE NEBULAE, E. Hubble. One of the great astronomers of our time presents his concept of "island universes," and describes its effect on astronomy. Covers velocity-distance relation; classification, nature, distances, general field of nebulae; cosmological theories; nebulae in the neighborhood of the Milky way; etc. 39 photos, including velocity-distance relations shown by spectrum comparison. "One of the most progressive lines of astronomical research," The Times, London. New Introduction by A. Sandage. 55 illustrations. xxiv + 201pp. 5⅜ x 8.
S455 Paperbound **$1.50**

HOW TO MAKE A TELESCOPE, Jean Texereau. Design, build an f/6 or f/8 Newtonian type reflecting telescope, with altazimuth Couder mounting, suitable for planetary, lunar, and stellar observation. Covers every operation step-by-step, every piece of equipment. Discusses basic principles of geometric and physical optics (unnecessary to construction), comparative merits of reflectors, refractors. A thorough discussion of eyepieces, finders, grinding, installation, testing, etc. 241 figures, 38 photos, show almost every operation and tool. Potential errors are anticipated. Foreword by A. Couder. Sources of supply. xiii + 191pp. 6¼ x 10.
T464 Clothbound **$3.50**

BIOLOGICAL SCIENCES

THE BIOLOGY OF THE AMPHIBIA, G. K. Noble, Late Curator of Herpetology at Am. Mus. of Nat. Hist. Probably most used text on amphibia, most comprehensive, clear, detailed. 19 chapters, 85 page supplement: development; heredity; life history; speciation; adaptation; sex, integument, respiratory, circulatory, digestive, muscular, nervous systems; instinct, intelligence, habits, economic value classification, environment relationships, etc. "Nothing comparable to it," C. H. Pope, curator of Amphibia, Chicago Mus. of Nat. Hist. 1047 item bibliography. 174 illustrations. 600pp. 5⅜ x 8.
S206 Paperbound **$2.98**

THE ORIGIN OF LIFE, A. I. Oparin. A classic of biology. This is the first modern statement of theory of gradual evolution of life from nitrocarbon compounds. A brand-new evaluation of Oparin's theory in light of later research, by Dr. S. Margulis, University of Nebraska. xxv + 270pp. 5⅜ x 8.
S213 Paperbound **$1.75**

CATALOGUE OF

THE BIOLOGY OF THE LABORATORY MOUSE, edited by G. D. Snell. Prepared in 1941 by staff of Roscoe B. Jackson Memorial Laboratory, still the standard treatise on the mouse, assembling enormous amount of material for which otherwise you spend hours of research. Embryology, reproduction, histology, spontaneous neoplasms, gene and chromosomes mutations, genetics of spontaneous tumor formations, of tumor transplantation, endocrine secretion and tumor formation, milk influence and tumor formation, inbred, hybrid animals, parasites, infectious diseases, care and recording. "A wealth of information of vital concern. . . . recommended to all who could use a book on such a subject," Nature. Classified bibliography of 1122 items. 172 figures, including 128 photos. ix + 497pp. 6⅛ x 9¼.
S248 Clothbound **$6.00**

THE TRAVELS OF WILLIAM BARTRAM, edited by Mark Van Doren. Famous source-book of American anthropology, natural history, geography, is record kept by Bartram in 1770's on travels through wilderness of Florida, Georgia, Carolinas. Containing accurate, beautiful descriptions of Indians, settlers, fauna, flora, it is one of finest pieces of Americana ever written. 13 original illustrations. 448pp. 5⅜ x 8.
T13 Paperbound **$2.00**

BEHAVIOUR AND SOCIAL LIFE OF THE HONEYBEE, Ronald Ribbands. Outstanding scientific study; a compendium of practically everything known of social life of honeybee. Stresses behaviour of individual bees in field, hive. Extends von Frisch's experiments on communication among bees. Covers perception of temperature, gravity, distance, vibration; sound production; glands; structural differences; wax production; temperature regulation; recognition, communication; drifting, mating behaviour, other highly interesting topics. "This valuable work is sure of a cordial reception by laymen, beekeepers and scientists," Prof. Karl von Frisch, Brit. J. of Animal Behaviour. Bibliography of 690 references. 127 diagrams, graphs, sections of bee anatomy, fine photographs. 352pp.
S410 Clothbound **$4.50**

ELEMENTS OF MATHEMATICAL BIOLOGY, A. J. Lotka. Pioneer classic, 1st major attempt to apply modern mathematical techniques on large scale to phenomena of biology, biochemistry, psychology, ecology, similar life sciences. Partial contents: Statistical meaning of irreversibility; Evolution as redistribution; Equations of kinetics of evolving systems; Chemical, inter-species equilibrium; parameters of state; Energy transformers of nature, etc. Can be read with profit by even those having no advanced math; unsurpassed as study-reference. Formerly titled "Elements of Physical Biology." 72 figures. xxx + 460pp. 5⅜ x 8.
S346 Paperbound **$2.45**

TREES OF THE EASTERN AND CENTRAL UNITED STATES AND CANADA, W. M. Harlow. Serious middle-level text covering more than 140 native trees, important escapes, with information on general appearance, growth habit, leaf forms, flowers, fruit, bark, commercial use, distribution, habitat, woodlore, etc. Keys within text enable you to locate various species easily, to know which have edible fruit, much more useful, interesting information. "Well illustrated to make identification very easy," Standard Cat. for Public Libraries. Over 600 photographs, figures. xiii + 288pp. 5⅝ x 6½.
T395 Paperbound **$1.35**

FRUIT KEY AND TWIG KEY TO TREES AND SHRUBS (Fruit key to Northeastern Trees, Twig key to Deciduous Woody Plants of Eastern North America), W. M. Harlow. Only guides with photographs of every twig, fruit described. Especially valuable to novice. Fruit key (both deciduous trees, evergreens) has introduction on seeding, organs involved, types, habits. Twig key introduction treats growth, morphology. In keys proper, identification is almost automatic. Exceptional work, widely used in university courses, especially useful for identification in winter, or from fruit or seed only. Over 350 photos, up to 3 times natural size. Index of common, scientific names, in each key. xvii + 125pp. 5⅝ x 8⅜.
T511 Paperbound **$1.25**

INSECT LIFE AND INSECT NATURAL HISTORY, S. W. Frost. Unusual for emphasizing habits, social life, ecological relations of insects rather than more academic aspects of classification, morphology. Prof. Frost's enthusiasm and knowledge are everywhere evident as he discusses insect associations, specialized habits like leaf-rolling, leaf mining, case-making, the gall insects, boring insects, etc. Examines matters not usually covered in general works: insects as human food; insect music, musicians; insect response to radio waves; use of insects in art, literature. "Distinctly different, possesses an individuality all its own," Journal of Forestry. Over 700 illustrations. Extensive bibliography. x + 524pp. 5⅜ x 8.
T519 Paperbound **$2.49**

A WAY OF LIFE, AND OTHER SELECTED WRITINGS, Sir William Osler. Physician, humanist, Osler discusses brilliantly Thomas Browne, Gui Patin, Robert Burton, Michael Servetus, William Beaumont, Laennec. Includes such favorite writing as title essay, "The Old Humanities and the New Science," "Books and Men," "The Student Life," 6 more of his best discussions of philosophy, literature, religion. "The sweep of his mind and interests embraced every phase of human activity," G. L. Keynes. 5 photographs. Introduction by G. L. Keynes, M.D., F.R.C.S. xx + 278pp. 5⅜ x 8.
T488 Paperbound **$1.50**

THE GENETICAL THEORY OF NATURAL SELECTION, R. A. Fisher. 2nd revised edition of vital reviewing of Darwin's Selection Theory in terms of particulate inheritance, by one of greatest authorities on experimental, theoretical genetics. Theory stated in mathematical form. Special features of particulate inheritance are examined: evolution of dominance, maintenance of specific variability, mimicry, sexual selection, etc. 5 chapters on man's special circumstances as a social animal. 16 photographs. x + 310pp. 5⅜ x 8.
S466 Paperbound **$1.85**

10

THE AUTOBIOGRAPHY OF CHARLES DARWIN, AND SELECTED LETTERS, edited by Francis Darwin. Darwin's own record of early life; historic voyage aboard "Beagle;" furore surrounding evolution, his replies; reminiscences of his son. Letters to Henslow, Lyell, Hooker, Huxley, Wallace, Kingsley, etc., and thoughts on religion, vivisection. We see how he revolutionized geology with concepts of ocean subsidence; how his great books on variation of plants and animals, primitive man, expression of emotion among primates, plant fertilization, carnivorous plants, protective coloration, etc., came into being. 365pp. 5⅜ x 8.
T479 Paperbound **$1.65**

ANIMALS IN MOTION, Eadweard Muybridge. Largest, most comprehensive selection of Muybridge's famous action photos of animals, from his "Animal Locomotion." 3919 high-speed shots of 34 different animals, birds, in 123 types of action; horses, mules, oxen, pigs, goats, camels, elephants, dogs, cats guanacos, sloths, lions, tigers, jaguars, raccoons, baboons, deer, elk, gnus, kangaroos, many others, walking, running, flying, leaping. Horse alone in over 40 ways. Photos taken against ruled backgrounds; most actions taken from 3 angles at once: 90°, 60°, rear. Most plates original size. Of considerable interest to scientists as biology classic, records of actual facts of natural history, physiology. "Really marvelous series of plates," Nature. "Monumental work," Waldemar Kaempffert. Edited by L. S. Brown, 74 page introduction on mechanics of motion. 340pp. of plates. 3919 photographs. 416pp. Deluxe binding, paper. (Weight: 4½ lbs.) 7⅛ x 10⅝.
T203 Clothbound **$10.00**

THE HUMAN FIGURE IN MOTION, Eadweard Muybridge. New edition of great classic in history of science and photography, largest selection ever made from original Muybridge photos of human action: 4789 photographs, illustrating 163 types of motion: walking, running, lifting, etc. in time-exposure sequence photos at speeds up to 1/6000th of a second. Men, women, children, mostly undraped, showing bone, muscle positions against ruled backgrounds, mostly taken at 3 angles at once. Not only was this a great work of photography, acclaimed by contemporary critics as work of genius, but it was also a great 19th century landmark in biological research. Historical introduction by Prof. Robert Taft, U. of Kansas. Plates original size, full of detail. Over 500 action strips. 407pp. 7¾ x 10⅝. Deluxe edition.
7204 Clothbound **$10.00**

AN INTRODUCTION TO THE STUDY OF EXPERIMENTAL MEDICINE, Claude Bernard. 90-year old classic of medical science, only major work of Bernard available in English, records his efforts to transform physiology into exact science. Principles of scientific research illustrated by specified case histories from his work; roles of chance, error, preliminary false conclusion, in leading eventually to scientific truth; use of hypothesis. Much of modern application of mathematics to biology rests on foundation set down here. "The presentation is polished . . . reading is easy," Revue des questions scientifiques. New foreword by Prof. I. B. Cohen, Harvard U. xxv + 266pp. 5⅜ x 8.
T400 Paperbound **$1.50**

STUDIES ON THE STRUCTURE AND DEVELOPMENT OF VERTEBRATES, E. S. Goodrich. Definitive study by greatest modern comparative anatomist. Exhaustive morphological, phylogenetic expositions of skeleton, fins, limbs, skeletal visceral arches, labial cartilages, visceral clefts, gills, vascular, respiratory, excretory, periphal nervous systems, etc., from fish to higher mammals. "For many a day this will certainly be the standard textbook on Vertebrate Morphology in the English language," Journal of Anatomy. 754 illustrations. 69 page biographical study by C. C. Hardy. Bibliography of 1186 references. Two volumes, total 906pp. 5⅜ x 8.
Two vol. set S449, 450 Paperbound **$5.00**

EARTH SCIENCES

THE EVOLUTION OF IGNEOUS BOOKS, N. L. Bowen. Invaluable serious introduction applies techniques of physics, chemistry to explain igneous rock diversity in terms of chemical composition, fractional crystallization. Discusses liquid immiscibility in silicate magmas, crystal sorting, liquid lines of descent, fractional resorption of complex minerals, petrogen, etc. Of prime importance to geologists, mining engineers; physicists, chemists working with high temperature, pressures. "Most important," Times, London. 263 bibliographic notes. 82 figures. xviii + 334pp. 5⅜ x 8.
S311 Paperbound **$1.85**

GEOGRAPHICAL ESSAYS, M. Davis. Modern geography, geomorphology rest on fundamental work of this scientist. 26 famous essays present most important theories, field researches. Partial contents: Geographical Cycle; Plains of Marine, Subaerial Denudation; The Peneplain; Rivers, Valleys of Pennsylvania; Outline of Cape Cod; Sculpture of Mountains by Glaciers; etc. "Long the leader and guide," Economic Geography. "Part of the very texture of geography . . . models of clear thought," Geographic Review. 130 figures. vi + 777pp. 5⅜ x 8.
S383 Paperbound **$2.95**

URANIUM PROSPECTING, H. L. Barnes. For immediate practical use, professional geologist considers uranium ores, geological occurrences, field conditions, all aspects of highly profitable occupation. "Helpful information . . . easy-to-use, easy-to-find style," Geotimes. x + 117pp. 5⅜ x 8.
T309 Paperbound **$1.00**

11

DE RE METALLICA, Georgius Agricola. 400 year old classic translated, annotated by former President Herbert Hoover. 1st scientific study of mineralogy, mining, for over 200 years after its appearance in 1556 the standard treatise. 12 books, exhaustively annotated, discuss history of mining, selection of sites, types of deposits, making pits, shafts, ventilating, pumps, crushing machinery; assaying, smelting, refining metals; also salt alum, nitre, glass making. Definitive edition, with all 289 16th century woodcuts of original. Biographical, historical introductions. Bibliography, survey of ancient authors. Indexes. A fascinating book for anyone interested in art, history of science, geology, etc. Deluxe Edition. 289 illustrations. 672pp. 6¾ x 10. Library cloth.
S6 Clothbound **$10.00**

INTERNAL CONSTITUTION OF THE EARTH, edited by Beno Gutenberg. Prepared for National Research Council, this is a complete, thorough coverage of earth origins, continent formation, nature and behaviour of earth's core, petrology of crust, cooling forces in core, seismic and earthquake material, gravity, elastic constants, strain characteristics, similar topics. "One is filled with admiration . . . a high standard . . . there is no reader who will not learn something from this book," London, Edinburgh, Dublin, Philosophic Magazine. Largest Bibliography in print: 1127 classified items. Table of constants. 43 diagrams. 439pp. 6⅛ x 9¼.
S414 Paperbound **$2.45**

THE BIRTH AND DEVELOPMENT OF THE GEOLOGICAL SCIENCES, F. D. Adams. Most thorough history of earth sciences ever written. Geological thought from earliest times to end of 19th century, covering over 300 early thinkers and systems; fossils and their explanation, vulcanists vs. neptunists, figured stones and paleontology, generation of stones, dozens of similar topics. 91 illustrations, including Medieval, Renaissance woodcuts, etc. 632 footnotes, mostly bibliographical. 511pp. 5⅜ x 8.
T5 Paperbound **$2.00**

HYDROLOGY, edited by O. E. Meinzer, prepared for the National Research Council. Detailed, complete reference library on precipitation, evaporation, snow, snow surveying, glaciers, lakes, infiltration, soil moisture, ground water, runoff, drought, physical changes produced by water hydrology of limestone terranes, etc. Practical in application, especially valuable for engineers. 24 experts have created "the most up-to-date, most complete treatment of the subject," Am. Assoc. of Petroleum Geologists. 165 illustrations. xi + 712pp. 6⅛ x 9¼.
S191 Paperbound **$2.95**

LANGUAGE AND TRAVEL AIDS FOR SCIENTISTS

SAY IT language phrase books

"SAY IT" in the foreign language of your choice! We have sold over ½ million copies of these popular, useful language books. They will not make you an expert linguist overnight, but they do cover most practical matters of everyday life abroad.

Over 1000 useful phrases, expressions, additional variants, substitutions.

Modern! Useful! Hundreds of phrases not available in other texts: "Nylon," "air-conditioned," etc.

The ONLY inexpensive phrase book **completely indexed.** Everything is available at a flip of your finger, ready to use.

Prepared by native linguists, travel experts.

Based on years of travel experience abroad.

May be used by itself, or to supplement any other text or course. Provides a living element. Used by many colleges, institutions: Hunter College; Barnard College; Army Ordinance School, Aberdeen; etc.

Available, 1 book per language:

Danish (T818) 75¢
Dutch (T817) 75¢
English (for German-speaking people) (T801) 60¢
English (for Italian-speaking people) (T816) 60¢
English (for Spanish-speaking people) (T802) 60¢
Esperanto (T820) 75¢
French (T803) 60¢
German (T804) 60¢
Modern Greek (T813) 75¢
Hebrew (T805) 60¢

Italian (T806) 60¢
Japanese (T807) 75¢
Norwegian (T814) 75¢
Russian (T810) 75¢
Spanish (T811) 60¢
Turkish (T821) 75¢
Yiddish (T815) 75¢
Swedish (T812) 75¢
Polish (T808) 75¢
Portuguese (T809) 75¢

DOVER SCIENCE BOOKS

MONEY CONVERTER AND TIPPING GUIDE FOR EUROPEAN TRAVEL, C. Vomacka. Purse-size handbook crammed with information on currency regulations, tipping for every European country, including Israel, Turkey, Czechoslovakia, Rumania, Egypt, Russia, Poland. Telephone, postal rates; duty-free imports, passports, visas, health certificates; foreign clothing sizes; weather tables. What, when to tip. 5th year of publication. 128pp. 3½ x 5¼. T260 Paperbound 60¢

NEW RUSSIAN-ENGLISH AND ENGLISH-RUSSIAN DICTIONARY, M. A. O'Brien. Unusually comprehensive guide to reading, speaking, writing Russian, for both advanced, beginning students. Over 70,000 entries in new orthography, full information on accentuation, grammatical classifications. Shades of meaning, idiomatic uses, colloquialisms, tables of irregular verbs for both languages. Individual entries indicate stems, transitiveness, perfective, imperfective aspects, conjugation, sound changes, accent, etc. Includes pronunciation instruction. Used at Harvard, Yale, Cornell, etc. 738pp. 5⅜ x 8. T208 Paperbound $ 2.00

PHRASE AND SENTENCE DICTIONARY OF SPOKEN RUSSIAN, English-Russian, Russian-English. Based on phrases, complete sentences, not isolated words—recognized as one of best methods of learning idiomatic speech. Over 11,500 entries, indexed by single words, over 32,000 English, Russian sentences, phrases, in immediately useable form. Shows accent changes in conjugation, declension; irregular forms listed both alphabetically, under main form of word. 15,000 word introduction covers Russian sounds, writing, grammar, syntax. 15 page appendix of geographical names, money, important signs, given names, foods, special Soviet terms, etc. Originally published as U.S. Gov't Manual TM 30-944. iv + 573pp. 5⅜ x 8. T496 Paperbound $2.75

PHRASE AND SENTENCE DICTIONARY OF SPOKEN SPANISH, Spanish-English, English-Spanish. Compiled from spoken Spanish, based on phrases, complete sentences rather than isolated words—not an ordinary dictionary. Over 16,000 entries indexed under single words, both Castilian, Latin-American. Language in immediately useable form. 25 page introduction provides rapid survey of sounds, grammar, syntax, full consideration of irregular verbs. Especially apt in modern treatment of phrases, structure. 17 page glossary gives translations of geographical names, money values, numbers, national holidays, important street signs, useful expressions of high frequency, plus unique 7 page glossary of Spanish, Spanish-American foods. Originally published as U.S. Gov't Manual TM 30-900. iv + 513pp. 5⅝ x 8⅜. T495 Paperbound $1.75

SAY IT CORRECTLY language record sets

The best inexpensive pronunciation aids on the market. Spoken by native linguists associated with major American universities, each record contains:

> 14 minutes of speech—12 minutes of normal, relatively slow speech, 2 minutes of normal conversational speed.

> 120 basic phrases, sentences, covering nearly every aspect of everyday life, travel—introducing yourself, travel in autos, buses, taxis, etc., walking, sightseeing, hotels, restaurants, money, shopping, etc.

> 32 page booklet containing everything on record plus English translations easy-to-follow phonetic guide.

> Clear, high-fidelity recordings.

> Unique bracketing systems, selection of basic sentences enabling you to expand use of SAY IT CORRECTLY records with a dictionary, to fit thousands of additional situations.

Use this record to supplement any course or text. All sounds in each language illustrated perfectly—imitate speaker in pause which follows each foreign phrase in slow section, and be amazed at increased ease, accuracy of pronounciation. Available, one language per record for

French	Spanish	German
Italian	Dutch	Modern Greek
Japanese	Russian	Portuguese
Polish	Swedish	Hebrew
English (for German-speaking people)		English (for Spanish-speaking people)

7″ (33 1/3 rpm) record, album, booklet. $1.00 each.

SPEAK MY LANGUAGE: SPANISH FOR YOUNG BEGINNERS, M. Ahlman, Z. Gilbert. Records provide one of the best, most entertaining methods of introducing a foreign language to children. Within framework of train trip from Portugal to Spain, an English-speaking child is introduced to Spanish by native companion. (Adapted from successful radio program of N.Y. State Educational Department.) A dozen different categories of expressions, including greeting, numbers, time, weather, food, clothes, family members, etc. Drill is combined with poetry and contextual use. Authentic background music. Accompanying book enables a reader to follow records, includes vocabulary of over 350 recorded expressions. Two 10″ 33 1/3 records, total of 40 minutes. Book. 40 illustrations. 69pp. 5¼ x 10½. T890 The set $4.95

CATALOGUE OF

LISTEN & LEARN language record sets

LISTEN & LEARN is the only extensive language record course designed especially to meet your travel and everyday needs. Separate sets for each language, each containing three 33 1/3 rpm long-playing records—1 1/2 hours of recorded speech by eminent native speakers who are professors at Columbia, New York U., Queens College.

Check the following features found only in LISTEN & LEARN:

Dual language recording. 812 selected phrases, sentences, over 3200 words, spoken first in English, then foreign equivalent. Pause after each foreign phrase allows time to repeat expression.

128-page manual (196 page for Russian)—everything on records, plus simple transcription. Indexed for convenience. Only set on the market completely indexed.

Practical. No time wasted on material you can find in any grammar. No dead words. Covers central core material with phrase approach. Ideal for person with limited time. Living, modern expressions, not found in other courses. Hygienic products, modern equipment, shopping, "air-conditioned," etc. Everything is immediately useable.

High-fidelity recording, equal in clarity to any costing up to $6 per record.

"Excellent . . . impress me as being among the very best on the market," Prof. Mario Pei, Dept. of Romance Languages, Columbia U. "Inexpensive and well done . . . ideal present," Chicago Sunday Tribune. "More genuinely helpful than anything of its kind," Sidney Clark, well-known author of "All the Best" travel books.

UNCONDITIONAL GUARANTEE. Try LISTEN & LEARN, then return it within 10 days for full refund, if you are not satisfied. It is guaranteed after you actually use it.

6 modern languages—FRENCH, SPANISH, GERMAN, ITALIAN, RUSSIAN, or JAPANESE *—one language to each set of 3 records (33 1/3 rpm). 128 page manual. Album.

Spanish	the set $4.95	**German**	the set $4.95	**Japanese***	the set $5.95
French	the set $4.95	**Italian**	the set $4.95	**Russian**	the set $5.95

* Available Oct. 1959.

TRÜBNER COLLOQUIAL SERIES

These unusual books are members of the famous Trübner series of colloquial manuals. They have been written to provide adults with a sound colloquial knowledge of a foreign language, and are suited for either class use or self-study. Each book is a complete course in itself, with progressive, easy to follow lessons. Phonetics, grammar, and syntax are covered, while hundreds of phrases and idioms, reading texts, exercises, and vocabulary are included. These books are unusual in being neither skimpy nor overdetailed in grammatical matters, and in presenting up-to-date, colloquial, and practical phrase material. Bilingual presentation is stressed, to make thorough self-study easier for the reader.

COLLOQUIAL HINDUSTANI, A. H. Harley, formerly Nizam's Reader in Urdu, U. of London. 30 pages on phonetics and scripts (devanagari & Arabic-Persian) are followed by 29 lessons, including material on English and Arabic-Persian influences. Key to all exercises. Vocabulary. 5 x 7½. 147pp.
Clothbound **$1.75**

COLLOQUIAL ARABIC, DeLacy O'Leary. Foremost Islamic scholar covers language of Egypt, Syria, Palestine, & Northern Arabia. Extremely clear coverage of complex Arabic verbs & noun plurals; also cultural aspects of language. Vocabulary. xviii + 192pp. 5 x 7½.
Clothbound **$1.75**

COLLOQUIAL GERMAN, P. F. Doring. Intensive thorough coverage of grammar in easily-followed form. Excellent for brush-up, with hundreds of colloquial phrases. 34 pages of bilingual texts. 224pp. 5 x 7½.
Clothbound **$1.75**

COLLOQUIAL SPANISH, W. R. Patterson. Castilian grammar and colloquial language, loaded with bilingual phrases and colloquialisms. Excellent for review or self-study. 164pp. 5 x 7½.
Clothbound **$1.75**

COLLOQUIAL FRENCH, W. R. Patterson. 16th revised edition of this extremely popular manual. Grammar explained with model clarity, and hundreds of useful expressions and phrases; exercises, reading texts, etc. Appendixes of new and useful words and phrases. 223pp. 5 x 7½.
Clothbound **$1.75**

14

DOVER SCIENCE BOOKS

COLLOQUIAL PERSIAN, L. P. Elwell-Sutton. Best introduction to modern Persian, with 90 page grammatical section followed by conversations, 35 page vocabulary. 139pp. Clothbound **$1.75**

COLLOQUIAL CZECH, J. Schwarz, former headmaster of Lingua Institute, Prague. Full easily followed coverage of grammar, hundreds of immediately useable phrases, texts. Perhaps the best Czech grammar in print. "An absolutely successful textbook," JOURNAL OF CZECHO-SLOVAK FORCES IN GREAT BRITAIN. 252pp. 5 x 7½. Clothbound **$2.50**

COLLOQUIAL RUMANIAN, G. Nandris, Professor of University of London. Extremely thorough coverage of phonetics, grammar, syntax; also included 70 page reader, and 70 page vocabulary. Probably the best grammar for this increasingly important language. 340pp. 5 x 7½.
Clothbound **$2.50**

COLLOQUIAL ITALIAN, A. L. Hayward. Excellent self-study course in grammar, vocabulary, idioms, and reading. Easy progressive lessons will give a good working knowledge of Italian in the shortest possible time. 5 x 7½. Clothbound **$1.75**

MISCELLANEOUS

TREASURY OF THE WORLD'S COINS, Fred Reinfeld. Finest general introduction to numismatics; non-technical, thorough, always fascinating. Coins of Greece, Rome, modern countries of every continent, primitive societies, such oddities as 200-lb stone money of Yap, nail coinage of New England; all mirror man's economy, customs, religion, politics, philosophy, art. Entertaining, absorbing study; novel view of history. Over 750 illustrations. Table of value of coins illustrated. List of U.S. coin clubs. 224pp. 6½ x 9¼.
T433 Paperbound **$1.75**

ILLUSIONS AND DELUSIONS OF THE SUPERNATURAL AND THE OCCULT, D. H. Rawcliffe. Rationally examines hundreds of persistent delusions including witchcraft, trances, mental healing, peyotl, poltergeists, stigmata, lycanthropy, live burial, auras, Indian rope trick, spiritualism, dowsing, telepathy, ghosts, ESP, etc. Explains, exposes mental, physical deceptions involved, making this not only an exposé of supernatural phenomena, but a valuable exposition of characteristic types of abnormal psychology. Originally "The Psychology of the Occult." Introduction by Julian Huxley. 14 illustrations. 551pp. 5⅜ x 8.
T503 Paperbound **$2.00**

HOAXES, C. D. MacDougall. Shows how art, science, history, journalism can be perverted for private purposes. Hours of delightful entertainment, a work of scholarly value, often shocking. Examines nonsense news, Cardiff giant, Shakespeare forgeries, Loch Ness monster, biblical frauds, political schemes, literary hoaxers like Chatterton, Ossian, disumbrationist school of painting, lady in black at Valentino's tomb, over 250 others. Will probably reveal truth about few things you've believed, will help you spot more easily the editorial "gander" or planted publicity release. "A stupendous collection . . . and shrewd analysis," New Yorker. New revised edition. 54 photographs. 320pp. 5⅜ x 8. T465 Paperbound **$1.75**

YOGA: A SCIENTIFIC EVALUATION, Kovoor T. Behanan. Book that for first time gave Western readers a sane, scientific explanation, analysis of yoga. Author draws on laboratory experiments, personal records of year as disciple of yoga, to investigate yoga psychology, physiology, "supernatural" phenomena, ability to plumb deepest human powers. In this study under auspices of Yale University Institute of Human Relations, strictest principles of physiological, psychological inquiry are followed. Foreword by W. A. Miles, Yale University. 17 photographs. xx + 270pp. 5⅜ x 8. T505 Paperbound **$1.65**

Write for free catalogs!

Indicate your field of interest. Dover publishes books on physics, earth sciences, mathematics, engineering, chemistry, astronomy, anthropology, biology, psychology, philosophy, religion, history, literature, mathematical recreations, languages, crafts, art, graphic arts, etc.

Write to Dept. catr
Dover Publications, Inc.
180 Varick St., N. Y. 14, N. Y.

Science B